No 9

RIVER PLANT COMMUNITIES –
REFLECTORS OF WATER
AND SUBSTRATE CHEMISTRY

N Holmes

and

C Newbold

Further copies of this report can be obtained from:
Interpretative Branch, Nature Conservancy Council,
Attingham Park, Shrewsbury SY4 4TW

ACKNOWLEDGEMENTS

This work was carried out as part of the Nature Conservancy Council's Commissioned Research Programme. The first author was employed between 1978 and 1983 on a contract entitled 'Classification of rivers based on their macrophytic flora'. The initiator of this project was the second author.

Many people have helped in the production of this document. Particular thanks are due to Margaret Palmer for her ideas on the original production of a Trophic Ranking System and for her comments on this manuscript.

CONTENTS

1.   INTRODUCTION   4

2.   RESULTS AND COMMUNITY CHARACTERISTICS   7

     2.1   Group A Communities   8

     2.2   Group B Communities   14

     2.3   Group C Communities   18

     2.4   Group D Communities   22

     Figures 1 and 2, and Tables 1-5   25-38

3.   DISCUSSION   39

     3.1   Appraisal of Ranking System   39

     3.2   Modifications and improvements to the
           Trophic Ranking System   42

     3.3   Validation of suggested modifications   43

     3.4   Value of Ranking System in Monitoring and
           Nature Conservation evaluation   45

     Figures 3 and 4, and Table 6   47-55

APPENDIX   A summary of the characteristics of the main
           communities and their distribution   56

1. **INTRODUCTION**

In 1979 **Newbold and Palmer** published, as **CST Note No 18,** their account of the **Trophic Adaptations of Aquatic Plants.** In that document 150 aquatic plants were assigned **Trophic Ranks,** species being sequentially listed from 1-150, starting with those confined to oligotrophic waters and working up to those tolerant of hypertrophic conditions. The publication aimed to facilitate a more objective appraisal of the trophic status of freshwater sites by simply referring to the Trophic Ranks of those species present.

The value of this system in evaluating the trophic richness of freshwater habitats is greatly enhanced because plant communities frequently give a far better understanding of the long-term chemical condition of a water body than 'one-off' chemical samples. Plant communities also give a far greater insight into the relationship between the soil, the medium in which the plants are rooted, and the water, the medium in which the shoots are bathed. Both fundamentally affect the composition of plant communities yet frequently it is only the trophic status of the water which is measured during routine chemical analyses. In some sites there may be a direct and positive correlation between the chemistry of the water and those of the substrate. In others there is not and in such cases it is more likely that the over-riding influence on the floral community will be exerted by the soil chemistry; the observed plant communities may thus lack a positive correlation with the nutrient status of the water.

The way in which plant communities can accurately respond to subtle variations in trophic status can be best illustrated by reference to a short stretch of the Basingstoke Canal near Eelmoor Bridge, Berkshire. In an area not exceeding two square metres can be found Potamogeton lucens (Shining Pondweed) growing adjacent to Scirpus fluitans (Floating Club-rush). The former is a species typical of eutrophic or enriched water, and hence its Trophic Rank of 124, whereas the latter is a species typical of acid and nutrient poor water, and hence its Trophic Rank of only 6. Conductivity and pH readings of the water amongst the two stands were identical (pH 7.75 and conductivity 550 umhos) yet pH readings of the substrate where the Pondweed grew ranged from 7.1 to 7.15 whereas the values for the substrate where the Club-rush was present ranged from 6.7 to 6.85. This clearly illustrates that the presence of the latter was in response to an atypical micro-niche afforded by a small area of oligotrophic sediment in an otherwise enriched environment. The plants were thus accurately expressing the true trophic status of the canal.

Since most assessments of freshwater habitats require a knowledge of their nutrient status, the use of macrophytes to indicate this is frugal in both time and money. Without taking a series of samples from both the water and the soil and on several different occasions, chemical analyses may be meaningless. Chemical analyses only represent one point in time and at one point and no matter how much replication there is, rarely can they consider the spatial variation within a 500 metre length of river. Plant surveys, on the other hand, reflect the inherent variability found within such a large area. Macrophytes, as trophic indicators, also have the advantage that they exist throughout the season and respond to changes in the condition of both the soil and the water. Single visits may thus suffice to indicate the trophic status of the habitat.

The document of Newbold and Palmer is also valuable in highlighting the trophic range of individual species. For instance, they show that some species occur only in a narrow range of chemical conditions whilst others span all the trophic categories. The former may be therefore regarded as good indicators whereas the latter may confuse assessments.

In 1983 **Holmes** published, as **Focus on Nature Conservation No 4,** his Report on **Typing British Rivers According to their Flora.** This publication summarizes plant communities found in over 1000 sites in more than 150 British rivers. In the Report there are descriptions of the 56 different plant communities which were identified using TWINSPAN, a computer program which classifies together communities with similar floristic characteristics. A summary of these findings is given in the **Appendix.**

The TWINSPAN analyses indicated clearly that riverine plant communities in British rivers could be divided into four main categories; lowland, enriched rivers with eutrophic plant assemblages (A), sandstone and limestone rivers, with meso-eutrophic plant assemblages (B), upland or lowland rivers on Tertiary sands or nutrient poor rocks with mesotrophic plant assemblages (C) and highland or lowland acid heathland rivers with oligotrophic plant assemblages (D).

Within these four main groups the analyses further divided the river sites into 56 types. A descriptive account was given for each of these communities in the Report, attention being drawn to features noted in the field or from maps. These included altitude, geology, water velocity, substrate and bank characteristics. These and many more environmental parameters were recorded in the field whilst other data have been accessed from other sources; they are now being given rigorous analysis to ascertain which of them have the greatest effects on riverine plant communities. This will be the subject of the next Report.

The Report also attempted to subjectively evaluated the trophic status of the 56 community types. These evaluations were assumptions based on the floral composition and a knowledge of the geology, there being no data available on the chemistry of the substrates or the water. Since no such data were likely to be available it seemed appropriate to make some subjective assessment of the trophic differences between the different communities.

The date presented here represents an attempt to objectively evaluate the trophic status of riverine plant communities by using the Trophic Ranks prepared by Newbold and Palmer. As far as we are aware it is the first time this system has been tested on data representing a large number of sites of a single habitat type. The river plant communities form an ideal data set on which to test the system because the individual community types were derived objectively. They were not derived with the aim of testing or evaluating trophic differences, and they are all communities of running, rather than standing, water habitats.

It would have been preferable to test the system by comparing with substrate and water chemistry data held by Regional Water Authorities. However since comparable data are not available for all Authorities, and more specifically for each of the 1055 sites, this was impracticable. In future this should be attempted. In the meantime this document is intended to illustrate the scope of the system and its possible value as a monitoring tool as well as its role in nature conservation evaluation.

An attempt has been made by **Haslam** (1978) to equate the distribution of individual species, rather than communities, to different nutrient regimes in both the water and the substrates of rives.

Detailed information gained by other workers is admirably summarised alongside the results of her own work. Of particular relevance are her 'star diagrams' that summarise the nutrient and base status of water held in deposits of rivers. Calcium, magnesium, chloride, phosphate-phosphorous, ammonia-nitrogen, nitrate-nitrogen, sulphate-sulphur, sodium and potassium characteristics are compared for rivers within flow over clay, chalk, hard sandstone, soft sandstone and resistant rock.

Haslam's data indicate that clay rivers have the most nutrient rich silts and their characteristic species are eutrophic. Chalk streams, on the otherhand, are described as mesotrophic because they have low magnesium, phosphate, chloride and sulphate levels. Because hard sandstone rivers produce a silt richer in these, Haslam categories this river type as having a higher nutrient status than Chalk streams. Soft sandstone rivers, on the otherhand, have low hardness ratios and high nutrient values (especially phosphate) giving a trophic status similar to Chalk streams. Rivers on resistant rock produces silts low in both nutrients and bases.

Haslam has also made use of water chemistry data collected by the former River Authorities and the River Purification Boards to correlate the distribution of individual species to different water chemistry parameters. Since Haslan has also collected her own data for nutrient levels within silt substrates, she has also been able to correlate the distribution of individual species to different chemical features of river silts. Although there are some close correlations between the two sets of data it is clear that the two are, more frequently than not, not related.

The data of Haslam firmly confirm our view that water chemistry alone cannot give a clear understanding of the trophic status of a freshwater habitat. The chemistry of the substrate is at least of equal importance in determining plant assemblages and, in a very high proportion of sites, and the more important determin. This is hardly surprising when it is considered that nutrient levels of water within silt have concentrations up to twenty times that held by the water outside the silt. However it is imperative to remember that nutrient status, whether in the water or in the substrates, is only one factor acting with many others to influence the floral communities within rivers. Rarely will it be the single most important determinand, substrate type, stability and geology, water depth and velocity, altitude and geographical location being likely to exert greater influence.

This publication should be regarded as a companion to the Report by Holmes since the data presented here supports many of the subjective observations concerning the trophic status of river types made therein. There has been a deliberate effort to duplicate only the minimum of information from it which facilitates a redimentary understanding of the data presented here. It is intended that these data complement those of the main Report and considerably increase our understanding of why the communities are discrete. (See Appendix for resume).

2. RESULTS AND COMMUNITY CHARACTERISTICS

The species which characterise the main groups of river plant communities are listed in **Table 1.** The Table lists the 76 species which have been assigned a Trophic Rank by Newbold and Palmer, there being a reduction of nearly 120 species from the original Table presented in the Report of Holmes because only aquatic higher plants have been assigned Trophic Ranks by Palmer and Newbold. At the foot of the page two **Trophic Scores** are given for each of the main communities; the upper one **(Trophic Mean Score)** is the mean value of all the Trophic Ranks for species which occur in **20%** or more of the sites which characterise the community, and the lower one **(Common Species Score)** is the comparable figure for species occurring in at least **50%** of the sites. The latter therefore only employs the more common species which, by definition, must be more obvious and therefore prefer, or tolerate better, the trophic conditions.

Comparable data for the 56 individual community types are given in **Tables 2-5.** In these Tables the Trophic Scores for **common species** include only those species which occur in at least **66.6%** of the sites representing the community type; the **Trophic Mean Score** are comparable to those in Table 1 and includes all species occurring in at least **20%** of the sites.

The number of species listed in the Tables vary greatly, there being 71 for Group A communities, 49 for Group B, 49 for Group C and only 29 for Group D. Compared with the original Tables given in the Report the numbers represent 54% of the total compliment of Group A 40% of Group B, 35% of Group C and 29% of Group D. These figures thus illustrate clearly the propensity of aquatic higher plants in Group A and the paucity of such taxa in Group D.

The differences in Trophic Scores for the main Groups is shown pictorally in **Fig 1.** The mean scores for the four Groups A-D are shown by horizontal lines and the scores for the four subsets of each are shown individually. The different results obtained by using only the common species (>50%) and all species (>20%) are also shown.

The Figure shows quite clearly that Group A has a far greater mean Trophic Score than the other three Groups, there being a 21% reduction in score to Group B, a 44% reduction to Group C and a 61% reduction to Group D. The figure also shows that the Trophic Score varies little in Group A when degrees of commoness are considered. However in the other three Groups the common species give a substantially lower Trophic Score. This is especially so in Group D, the most oligotrophic community, in which a 24% reduction in Score occurs when common species are used.

The Figure also shows the differences in individual Trophic Scores of the four subsets of communities in the four main Groups A-D. There is clearly a sequential fall in Trophic Score from A1 with a score of 112, to D4 with a score of only 39, with only three communities (B2, C2 and D2) not reflecting a perfect gradual decline.

Figure 2 illustrates the Trophic Scores of all the 56 community types using values calculated in Tables 2-5 using common species only. Again it is evident that there is a very clear reduction in Trophic Score on passing from community A1i with a score of 109, to Community D4i with a score of only 39. However, although there is a clear graduation from these two extremes the individual scores do not become reduced in an even manner throughout, there being some high scores next to relatively low scores.

The following section of this booklet explains why the Trophic Scores of Group A, B, C and D vary; it also explores why the individual community types within these Groups are also so variable. For clarity, a brief resume of the four community types described in the Report is given in the Appendix. This is accompanied by five maps which show the distribution of each of the 56 end-groups from the 1055 sites surveyed.

2.1   Group A Communities

The lowland communities of Group A were described in the Report as being "either base-rich or nutrient rich, and usually both". This trophic richness is confirmed in Fig 1 which shows that the mean Trophic Score for the common species (ie. occurring in at least 50% of the sites in at least one of the four sub-groups) of Group A exceeds that for Group B by 21%, for Group C by 44% and for Group D by 61%.

The Figure also shows that there is clearly a trophic difference between the four sub-groups of Group A; A1 is the most enriched community and there is a 25% decrease in Trophic Score down to sub-group A4.

Group A communities also have many more species assigned a Trophic Rank than the other three main Groups. This is because these rivers rarely support moss and liverwort communities, being dominated instead by aquatic and marginal flowering plants. In sub-group A1, for instance, 44 species contribute to an overall Trophic Score whereas the comparable numbers for sub-groups B1, C1 and D1 are 25, 15 and 17 respectively.

Individual community types (end-groups) show a wide trophic variation (Fig 2), ranging from 109 in A1i to 79 in A2ii. Despite this variation all but four of the 21 communities have higher Trophic Scores than the highest scores achieved in the richest communities of Group B.

Reference to Table 1 show that whereas 24 species are confined to being important components of at least one of the four sub-groups of Group A, only two species are confined to Group B, two species to Group C and four species to Group D. The 24 species exclusive to Group A have an average Trophic Score of 108, this being 10% higher than the Trophic Score derived from all species in Group A. Apart from these 24 species, the following are very much more common in Group A than in other Groups; Glyceria maxima (Red Sweet-grass), Lemna minor (Common Duckweed), Zannichellia palustris (Horned Pondweed), Potamogeton pectinatus (Fennel Pondweed), Apium nodiflorum (Fool's Water-cress), Sparganium emersum (Unbranched Bur-reed) and Nuphar lutea (Yellow Water-lily). These seven species have a Mean Trophic Score of 129, a clear indication of the rich nutrient status of both the water and the sediments of Group A.

Sub-group A1 - Enriched Sand and Gravel Rivers

These plant communities are the most eutrophic examples found in British rivers. This is very clearly illustrated in Fig 1. This Figure also shows that whereas most community types have lower Trophic Scores when the less common species are excluded, sub-group A1 shows an increase in Trophic Score. This suggests that the species which typify it favour enriched water and some are clearly tolerant of pollution. Further confirmation of the enriched trophic status of these communities is shown in Table 1; it shows that the three species assigned the highest Trophic Rank by Newbold and Palmer are all more common in sub-group A1 than in any other community type.

Care in interpreting the term 'pollution', as used here, is important. Its use here merely refers to an unnatural addition to the water of nutrients, and possibly other materials also. Such changes may be quite permissible in statutory water quality terms but for plant communities and wildlife It may be less satisfactory. One common effect is a reduction in species numbers, the most sensitive species being lost whilst the more robust species thrive and often become 'weed' problems. River sites which comprise sub-group A1 flow over very rich geological strata. Almost 20% comprise rich alluvial deposits and 44% is calcareous clay. Such high proportions are not found in any other sub-group. The Trophic Score derived from the Trophic Ranks of individual species thus confirms the view of Haslam (1978) that clay rivers are the most nutrient rich stream type.

Community A1i

This impoverished community was described in the Report as characteristic of "polluted, or at least considerably enriched" water. This description is particularly apt since the community has the highest Trophic Score of all the 56 end group community types. The high Trophic Score might have been predicted because it is characteristic of the extreme lower reaches of lowland rivers which flow in intensively farmed areas. Frequently the sites are affected by tidal influences. The sluggish velocity and deep water favour truly aquatic plants and the most successful species is the pollution tolerant Potamogeton pectinatus. This species has a Trophic Rank of 149 and it occurs alongside algae such as Cladophora, Vaucheria and Enteromorpha; these species also thrive in polluted waters. Few species with a Trophic Rank less than 90 occur in this community, the notable exceptions being Elodea canadensis (Canadian Pondweed), Agrostis stolonifera (Creeping Bent) and Phalaris arundinacea (Reed Canary-grass). These species were shown to have a wide trophic range by Newbold and Palmer. These generalist species therefore reduce the Trophic Score for the community.

Community A1ii

This community is similar in many respects to the previous one, the rivers being lowland, sluggish and dominated by aquatic flowering plants. It differs, however, in having more diverse substrates, and subsequently a more diverse flora, and not being affected by tidal influences.

The high Trophic Score is only marginally less than in A1i but most species with particularly high Trophic Ranks are less common than in the previous community type. Substrate variety increases species diversity, there being three species with Trophic Ranks below 60. Alongside these are species such as Nuphar lutea (Yellow Water-lily) and Sagittaria sagittifolia (Arrowhead) which have much higher Trophic Ranks but were absent from the previous community type. The most characteristic species of this community is Elodea nuttallii (Nuttall's Pondweed) a species with a very wide trophic range which can thrive in enriched water.

Community Aliii

This community is characteristic of intensively managed rivers which flow over sandy substrates. Compared with other communities of sub-group A1 this community has a low Trophic Score which reflects the relatively poor nutrient status of a sandy substrate.

Species with very high Trophic Ranks are therefore either absent or much rarer than in the previous community types; the most common species are generalist species with a wide trophic range. Indeed, all the species occurring in at least two-thirds of the sites comprising the community type are found in communities of Group B and occasionally in Groups C and D also.

Communities Aliv, Alv and Alvi

These three community types have almost identical Trophic Scores of over 100. They also have in common substrates which are a mixture of sands, gravels and clays. They also have calcareous water which is derived, at least partially, from underground limestone which is overlain by other more recent deposits. The water quality is generally good but enriched.

The similarity of the Trophic Scores for the three community types reflects a comparable richness of the water yet individual communities are very different. In general, therefore, the richer clay substrates and more sluggish velocity of Aliv is reflected in the abundance of species such as Sagittaria sagittifolia, Nuphar lutea, Potamogeton berchtoldii (Small Pondweed) Iris pseudacorus (Yellow Iris) and Scirpus lacustris (Common Club-rush). On the other hand these species are much less common in Alvi where the water is generally richer but the gravel substrates are less rich. Species such as Myriophyllum spicatum (Spiked Water milfoil), Zannichellia palustris and Ranunculus calcareus (Brook Water-growfoot) thus replace them.

Community Alvii

This community has a lower Trophic Score than the previous three community types because it is associated with less nutrient rich Tertiary sands. The Trophic Score, however, is almost 100 because the plants rooted in these intrinsically nutrient poor sands and gravels are bathed in calcareous and nutrient rich water. The organic matter carried by the rivers have also added nutrients to the substrates.

The relatively high Trophic Score in relation to the nutrient status of the solid geology is undoubtedly due to the success of species such as Potamogeton pectinatus, Potamogeton lucens (Shining Pondweed), Myriophyllum spicatum and Zannichellia palustris which have high Trophic Ranks. These thrive due to the nutrient richness of the water. However a very high Trophic Score is not achieved because these high Trophic Ranks are balanced by the low Ranks of species such as Equisetum palustre (Marsh Horsetail), Ranunculus fluitans (River Water-crowfoot) and Glyceria fluitans (Floating Sweet-grass), species which can thrive on the more nutrient-poor substrates and tolerate rich, but not polluted, water.

Sub-group A2 – Clay Rivers

The mean Trophic Score for this sub-group is just above 100, the second highest of the 16 sub-groups. The trophic status of clay rivers is thus intermediate between the rich East-Anglian rivers of sub-group A1 and the Chalk and soft limestone rivers of sub-group A3. Although clay accounts for more than 40% of the geology within the catchments of sub-group A2, soft sand accounts for 30%. Haslam (1978) suggested that rivers flowing over fertile sands have richer trophic characteristics than Chalk rivers; this has been confirmed by our data.

Reference to Table 1 shows that the most characteristic and common plants of clay rivers have Trophic Ranks exceeding 100, and usually above 120, the only exception being Veronica beccabunga (Brooklime) with a Trophic Rank of 76.

There is considerable variation in the Trophic Scores for the six individual community types of A2. Communities A2i, A2iii and A2iv have similar values but A2ii is 20% below this, A2vi 10% below and A2v 5% above this.

Community A2i

This impoverished community is associated with the highly managed clay rivers which have a solid geology comprising, at least in part, of soft limestone. Table 2 shows that eight species are more common in this community than in other communities of sub-group A2 but none are particularly noteworthy. Despite the impoverished flora, the species which are present reflect the typical Trophic Score of about 100 expected for a clay river.

Community A2ii

This community was described in the Report as anomolous because the majority of the sites which comprise it do not flow on clay at all. The considerably enriched water flows instead over Permian and Triassic sandstone and mudstone. Because of the substrate the classic species of clay rivers such as Nuphar lutea, Sagittaria sagittifolia and Scirpus lacustris are absent.

No species are more common in this community type than in any of the other A2 communities. The only very common species are those which occur throughout Group A and usually in Groups B and C also. By having such a low Trophic Score, community A2ii illustrates the effectiveness of the Trophic Scoring system because it has highlighted the paucity of nutrients and bases naturally held by the substrates over which the rivers flow.

Community A2iii

This community is associated with mixed substrates, but clay is usually present. The water quality is generally better than in the previous community but it is usually much more base rich.

The richness of the substrates and the basic water chemistry results in the flora having a Trophic Score of 99, a score typical for a clay river. At least one of the species typical of clay rivers occurs in all the sites but no sites contain them all. Instead these species occur with Ranunculus fluitans, Myriophyllum spicatum or other species which overall do not change the trophic expression of the river which shows an underlying clay influence.

Community A2iv

This classic community of clay has 11 species which are more common than in any other river communities associated with clay substrates in sub-group A2. Species with particularly high Trophic Ranks (ie <u>Potamogeton pectinatus</u>, <u>Myriophyllum spicatum</u> and <u>Zannichellia palustris</u>) are either absent or rarely common whereas occasionally species with low Trophic Ranks (ie <u>Carex acuta</u>; Slender Tufted-sedge and <u>Myosoton aquaticum</u>; Water Chickweed) are more common.

The water is rarely rich in bases and the average Trophic Score reflects the influence exerted by the richness of nutrients within the substrate. The Trophic Score is thus much higher in A2iv than A2i; this is because it is reflecting the nutrient status of the substrate and not the water.

Community A2v

The very high Trophic Score for this community is particularly interesting because it illustrates how the substrates and the water together act to mould the trophic expression of a plant community. In the Report it was noted that this community had similar clay substrates as the previous community type but differed by virtue of its more calcareous water. The nutrients in the substrates and the bases in the water act together to produce a plant community with a very rich trophic expression.

No particular species with very high Trophic Ranks are characteristic of the community, there being an almost imperceptible general shift to a high Trophic Score.

Community A2vi

This community, by virtue of having a Trophic Score 15% less than that of the previous community, illustrates how base poor water influences the trophic expression of plant communities on clay. The Report noted that clay was always the dominant substrate yet the river catchments were typically fed by streams draining acid Tertiary sands or heathlands.

The Trophic Score is more akin to that expected for the substrate than the water chemistry yet the lower score shows that water chemistry does have an effect.

Table 2 shows that whereas <u>Nuphar lutea</u> is the only classic clay river species to be common, species of neutral or acid soils, such as <u>Juncus effusus</u> (common Rush) and <u>Callitriche hamulata</u> (Intermediate Starwort) are at their most abundant in this community. These latter species, together with the more generalist species present, account for the much lower Trophic Score.

Sub-group A3 - Chalk Rivers

Chalk accounts for 76% of the rock types within the sites assigned to sub-group A3. Compared with all other lowland rivers which flow over basic or neutral geologies, the Chalk and Oolite rivers have the lowest Trophic Status (Fig 1).

Reference to Table 1 indicates that almost 20 species are more common in Chalk rivers than in any other river community types yet only three of these have Trophic Ranks exceeding 120. These are: <u>Phragmites australis</u> (Common Reed), <u>Typha latifolia</u> (Bulrush) and <u>Hippurus vulgaris</u> (Mare's Tail), all species shown in Newbold and Palmer to have very wide trophic ranges.

Reference to Fig 2 shows that communities of classic Chalk rivers such as the Itchen and Test (A3i) have higher Trophic Scores than the smaller Chalk rivers of Hampshire and Norfolk (A3ii). These rivers in turn also have higher Trophic Scores than the silted, enriched Chalk streams (A3iii) and the Chalk rivers of Dorset (A3iv).

The highest Trophic Score for the very clear Chalk rivers was unexpected but it results from the common occurrence of species such as Phragmites australis, Lemna minor, Hippurus vulgaris and Carex paniculata (Tussock Sedge) which have high Trophic Ranks. They consistently thrive only in the classic Chalk river community where there is both an abundance of nutrients and a very stable flow regime. These species illustrate how generalist taxa, when used in an objective way such as this, can possibly alter the fine tuning of trophic assessments. (For a practical modification see 3.3.)

The lower trophic status of small Chalk rivers and those suffering siltation is still surprising. It can be adequately explained only by considering the effect that the stable flow regime has in favouring those species with high Trophic Ranks which have their roots constantly bathed in a stream of fresh enriched water. It is possible that it does not truly reflect the nutrient status of the community types.

Communities A3i and A3ii

The physical characteristics of rivers associated with these two communities differ only slightly; the main differences are that the latter are generally narrower, have coarser substrates and the volume of water they carry and its stability is lower. Chalk alone is found within A3i whilst in A3ii Oolite, clay and alluvium together account for 40% of the geology. Both community types support the majority of classic Chalk stream species but the higher Trophic Score of the former reflects the general trend towards higher trophic expression in the lower reaches of catchments. It also shows that the coarser substrates of A3ii, noted in the Report, support less trophic rich plant communities than those of the fine gravels of A3i. As stated by Haslam (1978), it is the extent and quality of silt within the substrate which is important. In large, more downstream, channels with very stable flows it would be expected that rich silts would be deposited.

Reference to Table 2 shows that there are clear differences in the two communities if species occurring in 20% of the sites are considered separately from those which are much more common (occurring at least 66.6% of the sites). In the former case the Trophic Score is highest for A3ii but this is considerably reduced if the less common species are not included. This results from the absence of just four species with high Trophic Ranks: Phragmites australis, Lemna minor, Hippurus vulgaris and Carex paniculata. In other respects the communities are identical.

Communities A3iii and A3iv

The Trophic Score for both these community types are lower than in other Chalk river communities. Although identical scores are achieved using the commoner species, the score derived from using less common species is much higher in A3iii than in A3iv. The higher Trophic Score for A3iii results mainly from the occurrence of Zannichellia palustris and Hippurus vulgaris, two occasional species assigned very high Trophic Ranks.

Sub-group A4 - Lowland Ditch Floras

The trophic status of floral communities commonly associated with the canalised upper reaches of lowland rivers is considerably lower than that found in such rivers further downstream (Fig 1). This would be predicted since the upper reaches of rivers are less likely to be enriched from either urban or agricultural run-off. Deposition of nutrient rich silt is also less likely. Since the silt appears to be more influential than the water itself, this is probably the feature which limits the development of very enriched communities.

The Trophic Scores for the four communities vary little. The highest score is only 84 for A4iv, this being highest because the ubiquitous and highing Ranking Callitriche stagnalis is common.

2.2 Group B Communities

In the Report the communities of Group B were described as having a trophic status 'intermediate between the truly mesotrophic communities of Group C and the substantially enriched communitries of Group A'.

This is confirmed in Fig 1 which shows that the mean Trophic Scores for Group B are 20% less than that of Group A and 22% higher than Group C. Unlike Group A, the Trophic Score derived from using the commonest species usually show lower Trophic Scores than when all species are considered. Fig 1 also shows that there is considerable variation within the four sub-groups, B2 even having a Trophic Score higher than that for Ditch Communities of sub-group A4.

Although eight species with Trophic Ranks greater than 130 are represented in Group B, they are rarely represented throughout the range of all the individual community types (Table 3). This compares with 14 species with high Ranks in Group A and only 5 in Group C. Only 2 species with Trophic Ranks greater than 105 occur in at least 20% of the sites in each of the 4 sub-groups (Table 1). Their mean Trophic Score is 56, this comparing with a Trophic Score of 108 for the 7 species confined to Group A and 21 for the two species similarly confined to Group C.

Sub-group B1 - Lowland Rivers of NE Scotland

The mean Trophic Scores of around 80 for this sub-group reflects the typical trophic status of Group B as a whole. What is unusual, however, is that the Score derived from using common species alone is higher than that derived from using the total species complement (Fig 1). Reference to Fig 2 on the other hand shows that the three individual communities B1i, ii and iii all show the expected drop in trophic status when the less common species are excluded.

The most characteristic species of B1 are frequently also characteristic of B2 (Table 1) but in the latter species with a low Trophic Rank, such as Juncus effusus (Soft Rush) and Myriophyllum alterniflorum (Alternate-flowered Water-milfoil), are much rarer.

Community B1i

This community of the lowland rivers in NE Scotland has a low Trophic Score compared with other Group B communities; the rarity of eutrophic species was noted in the Report. This results primarily from the substrates being predominately weathered Metamorphic rocks rather than sandstone. These have frequently not been weathered into fine substrates and this limits colonization of species which require rich substrates.

The plant community is unusual because different micro-niches within the rivers are colonized by species with very different Trophic Ranks. For example, in sheltered alcoves or backwaters where finely weathered sediments accumulate, species with Trophic Ranks exceeding 100 occur; species include Glyceria maxima (Reed Sweet-grass), Polygonum amphibium (Amphibious Bistort) and Sparganium erectum (Branched Bur-reed). These high trophic expressions are counter-balanced by species with low Trophic Ranks which commonly occur on the coarse substrates within the channel; the most characteristic are Myriophyllum alterniflorum and Callitriche hamulata (Intermediate Starwort).

Community B1ii

This community has the highest Trophic Rank in sub-group B1 principally because it is highly correlated with soft sandstone which has eroded to form soft, rich substrates. Species with low Trophic Ranks are much rarer than in the previous community type.

Interpreting the Trophic Rank of this community illustrates how difficult it is to distinguish the primary causitive factors which effect changes in floral communities. Although fine sands are likely to contain more nutrients than coarser deposits of the same material, the fact that these rivers are likely to flow through cultivated land results in additional nutrients reaching the river which are likely to produce an increase in trophic status.

Community B1iii

This community has a Trophic Score intermediate between B1i and B1ii and this reflects its physical characteristics. The predominately earth banks confine the rivers to flow over rocks, pebbles and sand but the banks themselves are stable enough to be colonized. The banks therefore frequently have the species with high Trophic Ranks (such as Polygonum amphibium and Sparganium erectum) whereas the dominant species of the channel is Myriophyllum alterniflorum, a plant with a Trophic Rank less than 20.

Sub-group B2 - Enriched Lowland Sandstone Rivers

Only two community types are recognised, and both have Trophic Scores higher than other communities of Group B. Reference to Figure 2 also shows that their Trophic Scores are comparable to some communities of Group A. The high Trophic Scores were predicted in the Report by stating "The water, and/or sediments of B2 communities are more enriched than in other Group B communities." This was predicted because there is a combination of soft sandstone (43%) and limestone (36%) occurring in the lower reaches of these large rivers which are also enriched by silt deposition.

The trophic status of community B2i, characteristic of the lower River Tweed, is slightly higher than that of B2ii, characteristic of the lower River Eden. The key point to note is not one of such small differences between types but that both have Trophic Scores higher than would be expected for Group B communities. The Trophic Scores very accurately show that the trophic status of these rivers is more akin to eutrophic lowland river communities of Group A rather than the meso-eutrophic expression of Group B rivers. The classification derived from Twinspan shows that the species which characterise these rivers have more in common with other Group B river communities even though their trophic expression is closer to that of Group A. The objective derivation of the trophic status of this sub-group again confirms the view of Haslam that rivers on soft sand are trophically rich.

Sub-group B3 - Lowland Sandstone Rivers

Figure 1 shows that B3 communities illustrate the gradual decrease in trophic status of plant communities from Group A1 to D4. The figure also shows that the Trophic Score for sub-group B3 is lower than the mean for Group B as a whole, this being especially obvious when only the commonest species of the community are considered. The reason for this is clarified by Table I which shows that whereas species with very high Trophic Ranks exceeding 130 (such as Potamogeton crispus - Curly Pondweed, Potamogeton perfoliatus - Perfoliate Pondweed, Myriophyllum spicatum - Spiked Water-milfoil, Callitriche stagnalis - Common Starwort and Polygonium amphibium) are present but never common, the common species never have Trophic Ranks exceeding 105.

The four individual communities of sub-group B3 have Trophic Scores ranging from 69-86, communities B3i, ii and iii have similar scores but B3iv is considerably higher.

Communities B3i and B3ii

The Trophic Scores of these communities are similar, being 75 in B3i and 69 in B3ii. Almost 50 sites are represented, most in the richer lower reaches of rivers which rise at moderate altitudes. The Report noted that the substrates were likely to be richer than the water.

Whereas B3i rivers are characteristic of the sluggish reaches of rivers on Old Red Sandstone in the vicinity of Herefordshire, B3ii is more associated with fast-flowing rivers descending from the Pennines onto Millstone Grit. Old Red Sandstone is inherently rich in phosphorous and it would therefore be expected that the latter would have a lower Trophic Score. Two additional factors contribute to this. Firstly, deposition of fine, sandy substrates is likely to be less because of the increased velocity; secondly they carry a greater amount of oligotrophic water because they drain peat-clad hillsides. Table 3 confirms this lower trophic status and in addition it shows that the former is the preferred habitat for truly aquatic plants. Irrespective of the trophic conditions, these aquatic plants prefer finer sediments.

Community B3iii

This community has a Trophic Score of 72, marginally below the average for Group B. There are many rivers represented, the majority small, yet lowland and upland rivers are represented. The geology is generally rich, ranging from the complicated admixes of Anglesey and the Gower to the sandstone of Fife and the limestone of the Derbyshire Dales.

There are few species present which have been assigned Trophic Ranks, a feature which further illustrates that rivers of limestone dales have very poor aquatic higher plant communities in comparison with their more lowland calcareous counterparts on Chalk and Oolite. Despite this calcareous water, the flow regime is much less stable which results in a much coarser, nutrient poorer, substrate.

Community B3iv

This community is represented by only 3 winterbournes. Despite this the Trophic Score reflects the abnormally high trophic status of these sites in comparison with other Group B communities. This is a clear indication of rich geology, Chalk, alluvium and calcareous clay being the only strata.

Whereas the species complement of these sites gives winterbournes a Group B community instead of the expected Group A, their Trophic Score shows greater affinity to the latter than the former. This is because Group A communities are dominated by truly aquatic higher plants and the transience of the water in winterbournes precludes their development.

Sub-group B4 – Western & Upland Rivers on Sandstone or Limestone

The Report stated that "this group of communities comprises 4 sub-groups which are less nutrient rich and less basic than all other sub-groups of Group B." In general this is confirmed by the individual Trophic Scores and the overall sub-group Scores (Figures 1 & 2).

The main feature of sub-group B4 communities is that whilst they are associated with similarly rich geological strata the rivers rise at higher altitudes and flow more rapidly than other Group B rivers. The result is that nutrient rich silts are much less likely to be deposited. Sub-group B4 communities also occur further upstream, and thus at higher altitudes, than the other sub-groups; this usually results in these rivers receiving less urban and agricultural enrichment. These features combine to limit colonization by truly aquatic species, their role being taken by many bryophytes species instead.

Communities B4i and B4ii

The two communities are very closely allied to one another and have identical Trophic Scores. The former community is characteristic of small rivers on soft sandstone and the latter on the much harder calciferous Millstone Grit. Both communities occur at moderate altitude and both have very limited aquatic plant floras.

The flora of B4i is especially limited, there being only 12 species represented which have been allocated Trophic Ranks. B4ii on the other hand has 17. Both community types have only two species with Trophic Ranks exceeding 100 and these are not abundant or widespread. Sparganium erectum is one such species common to both communities. On the other hand the second species is Apium nodiflorum (Fools Watercress) in B4i and Myriophyllum spicatum (Spiked Water-milfoil) in B4ii. These two species indicate that the substrates of the former produces a finely weathered deposit in slack areas whilst the latter is more likely to be coarser but with a more basic chemistry.

Communities B4iii & B4iv

Both these communities have more species allocated Trophic Ranks than the previous communities. This can be attributed to both being very characteristic of lowland areas, the former with a scattered distribution whilst the latter is limited entirely to western Britain.

The higher Trophic Score of B4iii is exactly as would have been predicted since these communities are found in lowland rivers with mixed sand and clay substrates. Their low altitudinal sources allow some accumulation of silts but since these are derived primarily from acid sands, the common plants are rarely those that occur in base-rich rivers. The lowland landscape however allows productive cultivation and this raises the trophic status of both the water and the surface muds. These unusual conditions results in a strange admix of plants with very different Trophic Ranks, species such as Callitriche stagnalis, Apium nodiflorum and 4 other species with Trophic Ranks exceeding 100 occurring alongside species such as Myriophyllum alterniflorum and Callitriche hamulata which have Trophic Ranks less than 25. The former occur on the enriched deposits at the edges of the river whilst the latter are confined to the channel where less rich gravels and cobbles form the substrate.

B4iv has the lowest Trophic Score for any community in Group B. This is hardly surprising because all sites are found in large rivers downstream of more oligotrophic communities of Group C and Group D. Because the rivers rise at higher altitudes, and flow over much less rich geological strata, the plants which typify the community are ones most characteristic of gravels with a neutral chemistry. Species such as Myriophyllum alterniflorum are therefore abundant but the Trophic Score of the community is increased by generalist species which thrive along sheltered banks.

2.3   Group C Communities

The trophic status of Group C was described in the Report as 'oligo-meso/mesotrophic' being intermediate between the nutrient poor Group D and the richer Group B.

Reference to Fig 1 confirms this, showing Group C communities to have a mean Trophic Score of 55, this being 22 less than Group B and 17 more than Group D. The mean score for the whole Group as well as the sub-groups generally show considerably lower values when less common species are omitted. The Group thus confirms that the commoner species give a clearer view of the trophic status of a community.

Table 4 shows that 11 species with Trophic Ranks exceeding 100 are present in one or more of the 16 individual community types of Group C. However only five of these occur in more than three of the 16 representative types and only rarely are they common components of the communities. The generally lower Trophic Ranks of the species typical of Group C is further illustrated in Table 1 which shows that the ubiquituous Callitriche stagnalis (common Starwort) is the only species with a Trophic Rank exceeding 80 to be represented in at least 50% of the sites in at least one of the four sub-groups of Group C. This compares with eight such species for Group B and none for Group D. The two species represented solely in Group C have a mean Trophic Score of only 21, even lower than the species exclusive to Group D.

The above comparisons indicate that the overall trophic status of Group C is closer to D than B but individual community types vary considerably.

This latter point is illustrated in Fig 2 which shows the range from community C1ii with a Trophic Score of 69, to community C4iii with a score of only 44. These data support the distribution of Group C communities which were shown in the report to be frequently sandwiched between highland sites of Group D and the more lowland sandstone/limestone communities of Group B. The Report showed them to also predominate in the lower reaches of large rivers which traverse geological formations which are nutrient poor.

Sub-group C1 – Basic, Mesotrophic Upland Rivers

The Report indicated that this sub-group was the most enriched of Group C because the alga Cladophora glomerata indicated nutrient enrichment, and the mosses Amblystegium fluviatile and Cinclidotus fontinaloides indicated a high base content of the rock. This assessment is confirmed by the Trophic Score derived from the commoner species of higher plants present within the community; this results in the highest Trophic Score for Group C (Fig 1). The three individual community types have variable Trophic Scores but all are representative of mesotrophic plant communities found on rich substrata which might have been expected to produce meso-eutrophic communities.

Communities C1i and C1ii have relatively high Trophic Scores, particularly the latter, because they are associated with limestone or rich sandstone. The scores are based on the Trophic Ranks of only four species because aquatic flowering plants are rare due to the upland nature and rapid velocity of these rivers. Despite the paucity of species the Trophic Score accurately depicts these communities as uncharacteristically rich for Group C. They also illustrate how rapid current velocity reduces the trophic status of the substrate by washing out finely weathered material.

The much lower Trophic Score assigned to C1iii confirms the view expressed in the Report - "Wherever C1iii and C1ii communities occur in the same river system, the former always occur upstream of the latter. This indicates that the peat-clad mountains within the catchment makes the water more acid and less nutrient rich, yet the substrates are often as rich".

Sub-group C2 – Neutral, Oceanic Western Rivers

C2 Communities occur throughout Britain where shale is the dominant substrate; the community predominates, however, in the west. Fig 2 shows that C2i and C2ii have Trophic Scores similar to one another and 20% greater than those of C2iii, C2iv and C2v.

The Trophic Score of 61 for C2i is derived from just three generalist species, Phalaris arundinacea (Canary Grass), Caltha palustris (Marsh Marigold) and Agrostis stolonifera (Creeping Bent) since few aquatic plants are represented. This is because the communities are found in downstream sections of rivers which rise at moderate or high altitude. Frequently these rivers rise on moorland but an oligotrophic expression in the flora downstream is nullified by richer substrates derived from sandstone.

Communities of C2ii on the other hand nearly always support more aquatic higher plants because they occur in rivers with sources at lower altitudes. The richness of geology is similar to C2i but flash floods limit deposition of fine sediments. The community is unusual, as discussed in the Report, and a trophic status above average for Group C was suggested.

The Trophic Scores of C2iii-v are 20% less than those of C2i and C2ii. Almost all representative sites occur on neutral non-sedimentary rocks and therefore contrast with the two preceeding community types. The Trophic Scores therefore reflect the reduced trophic status of the substrates. This is particularly relevant for community C2v which has sluggish habitats and open banks which favour reed development at the margins. Despite this the species which colonize this habitat are those which are representative of oligo-mesotrophic conditions.

Sub-group C3 - Oligo-Mesotrophic Upland Rivers in England and Wales

The main feature which characterises this sub-group is stability, either in flow regime or substrate. The former category includes those communities found in upland bogs or below lakes or reservoirs whereas the latter includes those found associated with stable earth banks or where neutral clay is present. Such features are likely to allow finely eroded particles to be deposited in slack areas, or on sheltered margins, and allow a more diverse higher plant community to develop. Such a community is likely to have a trophic status slightly higher than the water chemistry would suggest because of the additional nutrients in the fine deposits. The Trophic Score of 61 for the sub-group confirms this, the Score being comparable to that of C1, a community type associated with far richer rock types but with little or no deposition of fine sediments because they lack physical stability.

Reference to Table 4 illustrates clearly how the stability of flow and/or substrates results in the presence of many more species of flowering plants; this is reflected by the larger number of species allocated Trophic Ranks by Newbold and Palmer. Although the Trophic Scores of C1 and C3 are comparable, the number of flowering plants allocated Trophic Ranks varies from 18 in the former to 39 in the latter. The differences are even more clearly evident if only the common taxa are considered, the number present in C1 being only seven compared with 21 in C3. This is also confirmed in Table 1 which shows that 11 species of flowering plant are more common in C3 than in any other sub-group of Group C; the comparable number for C1 is three. These 11 species have a mean Trophic Score of 66.5, higher than the mean for Group C because the majority are associated with the finer, richer sediments.

Differences in the trophic status of the five individual communities of C3 are shown in Fig 2. In this figure it is clear that there is considerable variation, C3i approaching true oligotrophic status whereas C3iii has a 30% increase in status from this; this can be regarded as borderline between mesotrophy and meso-eutrophy.

Communities C3i–iii

These three communities have much in common but differ in key ways which affect the trophic expression of their floras. In C3i the communities are associated with fine sediments as the uncharacteristically stable rivers traverse upland bogs and fens. The water is thus peat-stained and low in bases and nutrients; although the substrates are fine they too are relatively poor in nutrients and bases. Because the communities of C3ii and C3iii are below, and not part of the regulatory influence, these rivers tend to have much coarser substrates although sheltered margins allow deposition of some fine sediments. C3ii and C3iii have similar features but the latter normally occur where the volocity of the river is declining to enable much finer substrates to be deposited.

The Trophic Scores of the three community types illustrate how effectively the objective use of the Trophic Ranks can highlight subtle differences even in similar mesotrophic communities. The lowest score is assigned to C3i because these river communities are associated with upland bogs and fens (such as the River Teifi traversing Tregaron Bog and River Spey traversing Loch Insh Marshes). Here marginal and submerged aquatic plants thrive because of substrate stability, not nutrient enrichment. Although the substrates are much coarser in C3ii and C3iii these communities have higher Trophic Scores because they are at lower altitudes, and below the influences of agricultural development; this ensures that the limited fine deposits are richer than those of C3i.

The above points are clearly illustrated in Table 4 which shows that species with a low Trophic Rank, such as Carex aquatilis (Water Sedge) and C. rostrata (Bottle Sedge), are limited to being common in C3i. On the other hand species with a similar habitat preference for river margins, but with higher Trophic Ranks, such as Sparganium erectum (Branched Bur-reed), predominate in C3ii and C3iii.

Communities C3iv and C3v

The former community typifies small mesotrophic streams and rivers which drain shales and contain very few aquatic flowering plants. The Trophic Score is thus derived from the generalist mesotrophic species which grow along their margins.

The latter community, however, is especially associated with the New Forest. The strange admix of species which occur in the small rivers of the New Forest have a distinct mesotrophic expression This might have been expected from the geology of the area yet reference to Fig 3 shows that such a trophic status is atypical for lowland rivers in England. The Trophic Scoring System thus accurately reflects the distinctiveness of the streams which traverse these lowland heaths. Table 4 illustrates the atypicalness of the assemblage, with high Ranks from species such as Apium nodiflorum (Fools Water-cress), Callitriche obtusangula (Blunt-fruited water-starwort) and Alisma plantago aquatica (Water Plantain) being balanced by low Ranks from species such as Juncus bulbosus (Bulbous Rush), Ranunculus omiophyllus (Round-leaved Crowfoot) and Potamogeton polygonifolius (Bog Pondweed). Locally there are rich sediments, due to deposits of clay, and these areas have local patches where the flora expresses a much higher trophic status. Over a stretch of river as long as 1km, however, a truly mesotrophic expression is expected due to the interaction of the predominately nutrient poor sands and the acid water derived from the heaths.

Sub-group C4 - Oligo-mesotrophic Upland Rivers in Scotland

Reference to Figure 1 shows that the mean Trophic Score for this sub-group is slightly below the mean for Group C as a whole. Despite being characteristic of fast-flowing rivers, predominately in Scotland, the number of species allocated Trophic Ranks is equal to that of sub-group C3 and greater than in sub-groups C1 and C2.

The generally oligotrophic nature of the community is illustrated by the nine species in Table 1 which are more common in this sub-group than in other sub-groups of Group C. These species have a mean Trophic Score of only 43.5 compared with a Score of 66.5 for C3, the only other sub-group with a comparable number of species with preferance for single sub-groups. These data illustrate the clear relationship between the low trophic status of plant communities of gravel and shingle margins compared with the higher trophic status of plant communities of stable soils which can retain nutrients within their structure.

There is considerable variation in the Trophic Scores of the three end-groups of C4. In C4i and C4ii the Scores are comparable to other communities of Group C but C4iii has the lowest Trophic Score in Group C and can be regarded as truly oligotrophic. This is illustrated clearly in Figure 2. These objectively derived Trophic Scores confirm the following views expressed in the Report 'This community (C4iii) is typically up stream of either C4i or C4ii communities. Rivers are thus more upland and oligotrophic in nature and the influence of peat is obvious.' The Trophic Scores can therefore confirm that there is a gradual increase in trophic status on passing down even oligotrophic river systems.

2.4 Group D Communities

Group D was defined in the Report as being the most oligotrophic community type. This conclusion was based mainly on the lack of flowering plants and the richness of lichens and mosses.

Despite the paucity of flowering plants the Trophic Scores relect the oligotrophic water and relatively nutrient poor substrates. References to Fig 1 shows that the mean Trophic Score for the Group is much lower than the other three Groups. This is particularly evident when only the more common species are considered. Four species are confined to being important in Group D only and these have a mean Trophic Score of only 24.

Table 5 shows that only 29 species were recorded which have been allocated Trophic Ranks. The mean Trophic Rank for these species is 54; this is about 15% lower than the equivalent score for Group C, 30% lower than Group B and nearly 45% lower than Group A. Only four species had Trophic Ranks exceeding 100 and all these species are more common in the other Groups A-C. If the five species with the highest Trophic Ranks are excluded from the calculations, the remaining 24 species have a mean Trophic Rank of only 42. This is 25% lower than the comparable Trophic Rank of 56 calculated for Group C by omitting the five highest ranking species.

Within the individual community types of Group D (Fig 2) there is considerable variation. The lowest Trophic Score of only 34 is recorded for D3ii whilst its nearest neighbour, D3i, records the highest score of 50. In general the mean scores are lower than for any other individual community types but two end-groups of Group C also have scores lower than 50.

Community D1i

This community is characteristically the most species-rich community identified in British rivers yet it contains only 16 species assigned Trophic Ranks. Apart from the ubiquitous Callitriche stagnalis (Common Water-starwort) all the other species have Trophic Ranks below 80. This gives the community a mean score of 38, the second lowest recorded.

The generally mountainous distribution of this community type, found in association with shingle margins, ensures that the water is nutrient poor and the coarse gravels also hold few nutrients. The coarse river bed normally supports sparse populations of Myriophyllum alterniflorum (Alternate-flowered Water-milfoil) Callitriche hamulata (Intermediate Water-starwort) and Juncus bulbosus (Bulbous Rush), all species which thrive on low nutrient levels.

Community D1ii

This community is also associated with mountainous regions of Britain, but unlike the former community type, this community is normally associated with very stable, unshifting banks. This feature was noted in the Report which also identified the similarity with D4i. This similarity is confirmed by the Trophic Scores which are derived from far more species allocated Trophic Ranks than other Group D communities; 21 species in D1ii and 27 in D4i.

The oligotrophic nature of the water is clearly illustrated by the only common species associated with the community having low Trophic Ranks (below 60). Despite the stability of banks which support a much wider variety of marginal flowering plant than D1i, the Trophic Scores of the two communities are very similar because these additional species also have low Trophic Ranks. The only anomolous species with a high Trophic Rank is Sparganium erectum (Branched Bur-reed) which is a rare colonizer where fine, nutrient poor, silts are deposited at the margin.

Community D2i

In the Report this community was described as being ultra-oligotrophic since it is normally confined to the extreme upper reaches of mountain rivers. Despite this the Trophic Score is higher than in four of the six end-group communities of Group D. This results from so few species (only seven allocated Trophic Ranks) being recorded, the majority of which are resilient species which occur throughout Group D and other Groups too. Because of the harsh environment the typical oligotrophic aquatic flowering plants are absent and therefore cannot adjust the Trophic Score to reflect the true trophic status. In such rapidly-flowing and exposed river systems, dominated completely by bryophytes, it is impossible to get a realistic trophic assessment using flowering plants alone. (See 3.3 for assessment using modified system which relates more favourably to oligotrophic communities).

Community D3i

The relatively high Trophic Score for this community is higher than should be expected for Group D communities. This community occurs at lower altitudes than other Group D communities and the tree-lined rivers are associated with wooded valleys. The channels are generally narrow, which results in a shade impoverished flora. Truly aquatic flowering plants are therefore usually absent and the few marginal species found on the banks are frequently generalist species.

Community D3ii

The Trophic Score of 34 for this community type is by far the lowest identified in the 56 community types described in the Report. This is consistent with the description given, because this community type is associated with rivers which flow through uplands clothed in nutrient poor blanket-bogs. Callitriche stagnalis is the only species found with a Trophic Rank exceeding 62. Although there are only 13 species recorded which have been allocated Trophic Ranks, there is a good representation of oligotrophic aquatic plants such as Potamogeton polygonifolius (Bog Pondweed) and Juncus bulbosus. Emergent plants such as Carex nigra (Common Sedge) and Juncus effusus (Common Rush) are also represented.

Community D4i

This community has a very low Trophic Score despite having 27 species recorded which have been allocated Trophic Ranks. This results from the rivers generally traversing flat peat bogs which create slack water and finer sediments. These oligotrophic conditions are only successfully colonised by those plants which have been attributed low Trophic Ranks.

Fig. 1. **Trophic Scores** for each of the **4 main Groups (A,B,C & D)** of Vegetation types and the **4 sub-group** within each type. Lines represent the mean values for each Group whilst the mean values for each sub-group are shown individually. **Open symbols** and dotted lines represent the Trophic Scores derived from all species occurring in **at least 50%** of the sites in each Group or sub-group whilst **solid symbols** and unbroken lines represent mean Trophic Scores derived only from the species which occur in **at least 20%** of the sites. (See Table 1 for raw data).

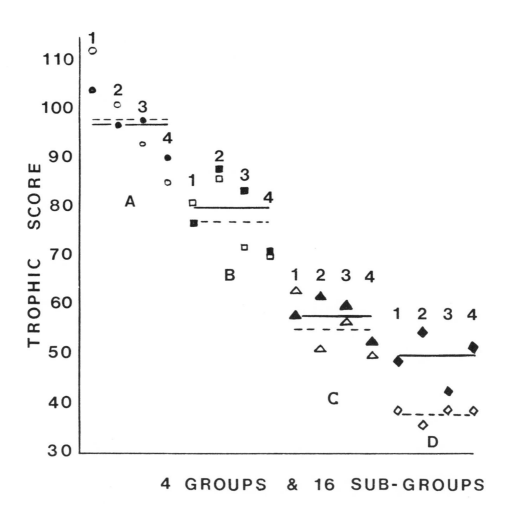

4 GROUPS & 16 SUB-GROUPS

Fig 2. **Trophic Scores** for the **56 individual community types.** Trophic Scores represent the mean of the Trophic Rank Numbers of species occurring in **at least 66%** of the sites assigned to each community type. (See Tables 2–5 for raw data.)

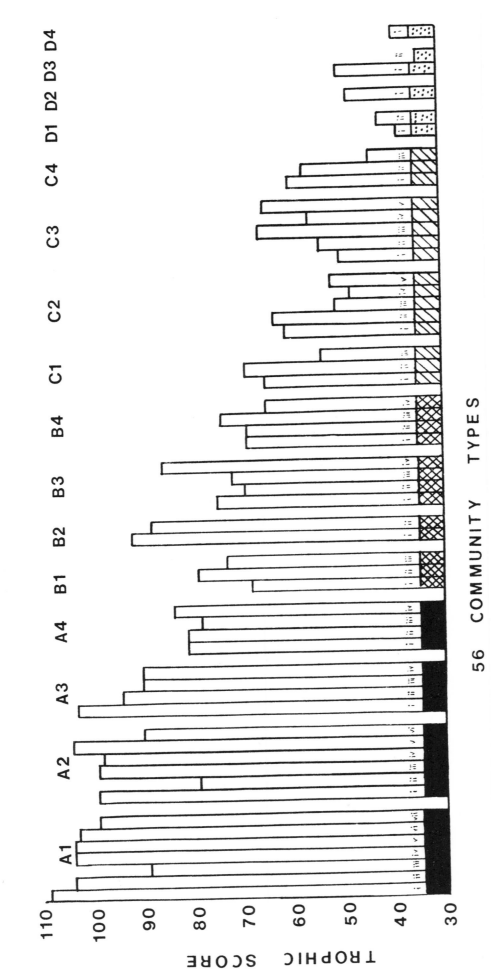

TABLES 1-5

Table 1. This Table gives information for all species which occur in at least 20% of the sites present within at least one of the **16 sub-groups** of river types. The Trophic Rank for each species is given in the left hand column and the occurrence of the species in each of the 16 sub-groups is tabulated as a percentage. At the foot of the Table two **Scores** are given for each sub-group. The uppermost one is the **Trophic Mean Score** which is the mean value of Trophic Ranks for all species occurring **in at least 20%** of the sites in each sub-group. The lowermost one is the **Common Species Score** which in the mean value of Trophic Ranks for all species occurring **in at least 50%** of the sites.

Tables 2-4 These Tables give similar information to Table 1 but these summarise the data for the **56 individual community types.** Data are tabulated in four Tables, information for each of the four main Groups being given seperately. As in Table 1, two **scores** are given at the foot of each Table but in these cases the **Common Species Score** is derived only from species occurring **in at least 67%** of the sites.

TABLE 1

RBSQ – 16 MAIN GROUPS

Species	Trophic Rank	A1	A2	A3	A4	B1	B2	B3	B4	C1	C2	C3	C4	D1	D2	D3	D4
Ceratophyllum demersum	144	28	6														
Oenanthe fluviatilis	107	30	6														
Potamogeton berchtoldii	92	22	5														
Ranunculus circinatus	98	21	9														
Lemna gibba	88	20	10														
Potamogeton lucens	124	31	17														
Elodea nuttallii	72	21	19														
Sagittaria sagittifolia	127	49	47														
Rorippa amphibia	112	19	**54**														
Berula erecta	81	35	11	**84**	37												
Callitriche obtusangula	83	10	28	**84**	29												
Ranunculus sceleratus	111	29	45	11	23												
Rumex hydrolapathum	100	28	19	46	3												
Veronica catenata	67	31	36	20	16												
Veronica anagallis–aquatica	66	46	29	**85**	33												
Carex acutiformis	110	43	39	**90**	28												
Carex riparia	114	**57**	49	**65**	12												
Phragmites australis	140	43	16	**52**	10												
Scirpus lacustris	142	42	**64**	25	3												
Typha latifolia	146	21	16	33	6												
Hippurus vulgaris	147			41	0												
Carex paniculata	113			47	8												
Catabrosa aquatica	86			20	5												
Groenlandia densa	117			30	2												
Glyceria maxima	116	**73**	56	79	25	29	10										
Lemna minor	139	**58**	41	**53**	23	37	26										
Zannichellia palustris	150	**64**	21	46	29	8	26										
Potamogeton pectinatus	149	**76**	**52**			6	23										
Butomus umbellatus	82	34	29			0	36										
Carex acuta	40	1	25			9	36										
Potamogeton natans	74	11	28			20	13					27					
Potamogeton gramineus	64					14	20						13				
Apium nodiflorum	106	**75**	**50**	**93**	79			35	23								
Myosoton aquaticum	37	14	33	4	21			32	2								
Polygonum amphibium	141	**50**	**67**	39	28	**62**	**80**	34	7								

RBSQ – 16 MAIN GROUPS

	Trophic Rank	A1	A2	A3	A4	B1	B2	B3	B4	C1	C2	C3	C4	D1	D2	D3	D4
Ranunculus calcareus	99	42	32	**88**	25	11	**60**	44	28								
Elodea canadensis	71	**74**	63	52	16	**74**	**96**	41	39								
Potamogeton crispus	137	**54**	39	19	20	**62**	**80**	24	19								
Ranunculus fluitans	45	30	30			16	**93**	**53**	12								
Potamogeton perfoliatus	135	**53**	29			20	**50**	23	3								
Ranunculus peltatus	48					20	1										
Glyceria plicata	42	69	42	25	30			25	5								
Myriophyllum spicatum	148	**88**	**94**	33	8	1	**63**	32	7								
Sparganium erectum	103			**95**	**84**	**96**	**96**	**77**	**59**	14	30	**70**	48				
Cardamine amara	30									23	8						
Alisma plantago-aquatica	109	28	58	12	38	22	40	33	25			25	5				
Rorippa nasturtium-aquaticum	97	**84**	67	**87**	**73**	**56**	46	**59**	8			21	29				
Ranunculus penicillatus	69					4	30	1	21	0	30	25	1				
Veronica beccabunga	76	**78**	**83**	**81**	**82**	**69**	**73**	**81**	39	49	23	33	40	24	0		
Glyceria fluitans	47	40	34	25	42	**62**	**50**	45	**57**	44	**64**	**97**	**87**	**89**	0	57	**94**
Iris pseudacorus	60	37	27	**79**	30	33	23			3	20	42	16			0	21
Phalaris arundinacea	78	**98**	**96**	**100**	**91**	**98**	**100**	**98**	**90**	**68**	**86**	**85**	**67**			5	36
Juncus effusus	51	19	54	39	67	**90**	23	48	36	**60**	**66**	**92**	**77**	**89**	66	**90**	**94**
Sparganium emersum	102	**70**	**77**	33	24			6	24			39	5			0	21
Nuphar lutea	138	**50**	**72**													1	21
Callitriche stagnalis	143	**59**	54	**77**	**69**	**72**	48	32	26	22	35	**65**	**50**	45	20	21	36
Mentha aquatica	77	**84**	**75**	**98**	**87**	**96**	**93**	**91**	**86**	**82**	**70**	**89**	**89**	**48**	6	17	47
Myosotis scorpioides	62	**92**	**95**	**96**	**91**	**98**	**96**	**97**	**54**	**63**	44	**66**	**96**	**62**	13	21	**63**
Agrostis stolonifera	53	**97**	**96**	**90**	**98**	**100**	**100**	**97**	**100**	**96**	**97**	**98**	**92**	**100**	46	**67**	**68**
Caltha palustris	54			44	25	**77**	**60**	**54**	45	**73**	**58**	**60**	**87**	**89**	20	28	**68**
Callitriche hamulata	23					41	0	11	23	20	**52**	**74**	**54**	**56**	0	25	**73**
Myriophyllum alterniflorum	18					**72**	36	1	29	26	47	**66**	**90**	**67**	0	21	**84**
Eleocharis palustris	56					48	**83**	23	24	25	21	31	**65**			1	**68**
Equisetum fluviatile	57					29	10					37	41	27	0	3	**78**
Equisetum palustre	58							22	43	31	25	16	25			13	31
Ranunculus flammula	26									41	**59**	**71**	**80**	**94**	40	**69**	**89**
Carex nigra	14									30	9	9	**69**	**81**	53	59	**94**
Carex aquatilis	12											21	23				
Ranunculus omiophyllus	19											33	3	24	0	21	31
Littorella uniflora	61											13	25			9	**52**

RBSQ – 16 MAIN GROUPS

	Trophic Rank	A1	A2	A3	A4	B1	B2	B3	B4	C1	C2	C3	C4	D1	D2	D3	D4
Carex rostrata	22										25	60	45	0	11	89	
Juncus bulbosus	44											36	48	89	66	73	100
Potamogeton polygonifolius	4													21	0	34	63
Hydrocotyle vulgaris	59															11	26
Veronica scutellata	27															7	36
Sparganium angustifolium	7															5	21
Total Trophic Mean Score		104	97	98	90	77	88	84	71	58	62	61	57	49	55	43	52
Common Species Score		**112**	**101**	**93**	**85**	**81**	**86**	**72**	**70**	**63**	**51**	**61**	**52**	**39**	**36**	**39**	**39**

TABLE 2

RBSQ-A

	Trophic Rank	AIi	AIii	AIiii	AIiv	AIv	AIvi	AIvii	A2i	A2ii	A2iii	A2iv	A2v	A2vi	A3i	A3ii	A3iii	A3iv	A4i	A4ii	A4iii	A4iv
Scirpus maritimus	128	25																				
Potamogeton pusillus	95	42																				
Potamogeton friesii	123	42																				
Elodea nuttallii	72	58							46				22									
Ceratophyllum demersum	144	**75**	**73**			24		30			23											
Ranunculus circinatus	98	50	55		50	24					23											
Potamogeton perfoliatus	135	**67**	36	29		52	**77**	70	54	22	38	38	38									
Potamogeton pectinatus	149	**100**	64	54	33	**86**	77	**100**	**85**	57	62	56		27								
Butomus umbellatus	82	33	73		33	38	27	70				**72**			40							
Potamogeton lucens	124	42	55			41		**90**	62	43	54	36	25									
Rorippa amphibia	112	25	36	21		24	32				23	**74**	47									
Rumex hydrolapathum	100	25	45	29	33	24	36	30				23	34		**93**	**73**						
Sagittaria sagittifolia	127		**100**	33	67	59	45	60	31	22	38	**79**	63									
Nuphar lutea	138		**91**		**83**	**76**	27	40	38		54	**100**	**94**	**82**								
Oenanthe fluviatilis	107		27		67	45	45	20							53							
Lemna gibba	88		27				27	70				31										
Potamogeton berchtoldii	92		27		67	38		30							20							
Phragmites australis	140	42	36		83	48	50	**80**					31	27	**80**	40	38	58				
Myriophyllum spicatum	148	**83**	73	50		59	**100**	**100**		30	**69**	38	59	36	20	60	33		21			
Potamogeton alpinus	73				50																	
Cardamine amara	30					21																
Ranunculus trichophyllus	75					21				22	46											
Equisetum palustre	58						32	40														
Azolla filiculoides	80							50														
Eleocharis palustris	56							20														
Potamogeton nodosus	125										23											
Alisma lanceolatum	108										23											
Carex acuta	40								46		31	49		45								
Ranunculus peltatus	48																					
Scirpus lacustris	142		36	21	83	59	68	60	62	43	69	**89**	**91**		53	20						
Ranunculus fluitans	45		36	21	33		50	80	62	22	**77**	56	34					25				
Myosoton aquaticum	37							20						36						42		
Typha latifolia	146				33		23	20			38		25	27	33	47	20					
Zannichellia palustris	150			63	50	**79**	**91**	**90**	46	43	23	51	22		**87**	**67**	29		43	21		55
Ranunculus sceleratus	111		55	29	33	45			**69**				50				29			53		27

RBSQ-A	Trophic Rank	AII (A1i)	AIii	AIiii	AIiv	AIv	AIvi	AIvii	A2i	A2ii	A2iii	A2iv	A2v	A2vi	A3i	A3ii	A3iii	A3iv	A4i	A4ii	A4iii	A4iv
Berula erecta	81		55		67	45	50	80	69	43			41		93	87	81	75			27	
Glyceria plicata	42			27	21			50							27	47	29	33	36	47	27	
Elodea canadensis	71	92	73	63	67	76	77	40	54	39	69	69	72	45	93	67	33	42	25	21		
Carex riparia	114	25	73	33	100	93	41		31			74	78		67		67	58		26		
Veronica catenata	67	25	55		33	38	27	30	54			67	50		20		29	33	25	32	64	
Veronica anagallis-aquatica	66	33	36	42		55	73				23	23	44	45	87	93	71	100	39	26	55	
Lemna minor	139	83	73	71	100	62	32	100	77	39	23	59	25		80	47	29	75	29			
Glyceria maxima	116	75	100	33	50	86	82	70	77		23	82	72		80	80	90	58	43			20
Polygonum amphibium	141	75	82	38	83	24	50	40	77	48	69	90	72		73	40	24	25	32	32	27	20
Callitriche stagnalis	143	25	55	46	83	83	68	80	31	26		62	81	91	60	80	90	75	57	63	64	95
Apium nodiflorum	106	33	82	75	100	83	77	100	54	35	23	56	69	36	100	87	90	100	89	74	82	70
Mentha aquatica	77	67	73	63	100	93	100	100	62	43	85	79	94	82	100	100	100	92	93	79	91	85
Myosotis scorpioides	62	67	82	92	100	100	100	100	92	87	92	97	100	100	100	100	100	83	93	95	82	90
Rorippa nasturtium-aquaticum	97	58	82	92	83	90	86	80	92	35	38	72	97	45	93	80	86	92	79	79	99	50
Veronica beccabunga	76	33	82	79	100	79	86	80	85	83	69	90	94	55	80	87	86	100	86	89	91	65
Agrostis stolonifera	53	100	100	100	100	93	95	100	100	96	100	100	91	100	87	80	100	92	100	95	100	100
Phalaris arundinacea	78	100	100	96	100	100	95	100	92	96	100	97	97	100	100	100	100	100	93	79	100	95
Sparganium erectum	103	50	100	83	100	93	95	100	92	83	100	97	97	91	100	100	90	92	86	79	73	95
Glyceria fluitans	47		45	42	50	31	45	90	46	43	31	41	22	55			33	58	64	21		50
Ranunculus calcareus	99		20	29	50	52	82	70	31		54	23	47	55	100	93	81	83	39			40
Callitriche obtusangula	83		36	21	83	31	68	30	23			26	59	64	100	93	81	75	36		27	50
Alisma plantago-aquatica	109		45	38	50	41	59	20	69	43	62	72	63	36	33	20			32		45	50
Potamogeton crispus	137		45	63	83	66		50	38	39	38	36	34		53	40			21			20
Sparganium emersum	102		64	54	50	100	82	60	77	70	62	87	84	100	20	60			21	53		60
Juncus effusus	51			29	67	23	23			52		62	47		20		57		64		73	85
Iris pseudacorus	60		36		50	48	41					28	50	27	87	73	76	83	57			30
Carex acutiformis	110		45		33	55	64						31		100	87	95	75	50	21		
Hippuris vulgaris	147				67										73	47	38					
Lemna trisulca	89														60							
Groenlandia densa	117			21					23						53	33	24	25				
Carex paniculata	113	25		21												53	33					
Potamogeton natans	74			21	50							38	28	64	80							30
Equisetum fluviatile	57				33										53	20						25
Callitriche hamulata	23													45								20

RBSQ-A

	A1i	A1ii	A1iii	A1iv	A1v	A1vi	A1vii	A2i	A2ii	A2iii	A2iv	A2v	A2vi	A3i	A3ii	A3iii	A3iv	A4i	A4ii	A4iii	A4iv
algae	3	4	4	3	4	3	3	4	3	4	4	3	2	4	5	3	3	4	3	4	3
lichens						1			1	1				1	1	1	1	1	1	1	1
liverworts		1	2	1		1				3	1	2	4	1	1	1	1	4	4	4	5
mosses		1		2	4	5	1	2	4	6	4	4	2	3	5	5	3	5	4	3	3
vascular cryptogams				1		1	3	1	2	1	1		2	1	2	1	1	1	1	2	3
dicotyledons	20	35	26	31	35	35	35	26	33	30	36	35	32	38	32	29	26	27	23	23	28
monocotyledons	21	27	22	24	23	24	29	26	15	21	27	26	16	26	23	19	19	18	16	11	15
	44	68	54	62	66	70	71	59	58	66	73	70	60	74	69	59	54	60	52	48	58
Total Trophic Mean Score	106	102	98	100	103	101	100	98	97	103	98	104	92	101	105	99	90	94	97	94	86
Common Species Score	**109**	**104**	**89**	**104**	**104**	**103**	**99**	**99**	**79**	**99**	**98**	**104**	**90**	**103**	**93**	**90**	**90**	**81**	**81**	**78**	**84**

TABLE 3

RBSQ-B

	Trophic Rank	B1i	B1ii	B1iii	B2i	B2ii	B3i	B3ii	B3iii	B3iv	B4i	B4ii	B4iii	B4iv
Equisetum fluviatile	57	57												
Potamogeton alpinus	73	43												
Carex rostrata	22	29												
Glyceria maxima	116	52	25											
Potamogeton gramineus	64	38				50	52	26						
Potamogeton natans	74	38				25		33						
Potamogeton perfoliatus	135	43			39	67								
Ranunculus aquatilis	70			29	33		29							
Potamogeton pectinatus	149		20			58	33							
Zannichellia palustris	150		25		33					100				
Rorippa nasturtium–aquaticum	97	71	70	29		67	48	44	77					
Polygonum amphibium	141	62	45	81	78	83	62	33	20					
Carex acuta	40			29		67								
Butomus umbellatus	82					67								
Cardamine amara	30					33								
Myosoton aquaticum	37						48	26	37					
Myriophyllum spicatum	148	76	85	24	56	75	62	44	20			21		
Ranunculus fluitans	45	62	30	48	89	100	86	70	93					
Veronica beccabunga	76	48	60	20	61	92	71	78		66	65	29	47	38
Lemna minor	139	76	80	80	33		24	22		66			32	33
Potamogeton crispus	137	48	60	62	83	75		41	23			21	58	24
Callitriche stagnalis	143	76	80	29	39	50			53	66			36	52
Callitriche hamulata	23	67	30											
Myriophyllum alterniflorum	18	81	40	95	50		29					29	37	67
Iris pseudacorus	60	52	25	24		33						21	26	24
Elodea canadensis	71	62	75	86	100	92	52	67				54	21	76
Eleocharis palustris	56	33	20	76	89	75	24	37	20			43		43
Caltha palustris	54	81	80	71	50	75		70	67		31	57	31	62
Sparganium erectum	103	100	95	95	100	92	95	70	80		31	50	89	86
Mentha aquatica	77	95	95	100	89	100	90	85	97	100	79	89	95	86
Myosotis scorpioides	62	95	100	100	94	100	95	100	97	100	55	61	63	38
Agrostis stolonifera	53	100	100	100	100	100	100	96	100	66	100	100	100	100
Glyceria fluitans	47	81	35	71	61	33	33	41	57	66	48	39	74	81
Phalaris arundinacea	78	95	100	100	100	100	100	96	100	100	76	96	95	100
Juncus effusus	51	86	95	90	33	100	48	26	70	33	41	20	68	24

RBSQ-B	Trophic Rank	B1i	B1ii	B1iii	B2i	B2ii	B3i	B3ii	B3iii	B3iv	B4i	B4ii	B4iii	B4iv
Sparganium emersum	102	33											58	43
Ranunculus calcareus	99				**78**	33	43	44	47	33	27	50	21	48
Alisma plantago-aquatica	109			38	39	42	**67**	33					42	33
Ranunculus flammula	26			24										
Ranunculus penicillatus	69					**75**								**81**
Rorippa amphibia	112						50							
Ranunculus sceleratus	111						29							
Veronica anagallis-aquatica	66		45						27	**100**				
Glyceria plicata	42						43		33	33				
Apium nodiflorum	106						48		50	**100**	21		**68**	
Veronica catenata	67									33				
Equisetum palustre	58						24	22	23		38	57	21	62
Callitriche obtusangula	83									33				
Potamogeton berchtoldii	92												21	33
algae		6	6	7	8	7	6	7	5	5	5	7	5	7
lichens		2	1	3	2	2	1	1	1	1	1	1	1	1
liverworts		1	3	5	2	2	4	5	6	3	5	4	6	5
mosses		7	6	10	9	8	8	8	8	9	10	9	7	9
vascular cryptogams		3	2	2	2	1	2	2	3	-	3	3	2	2
dicotyledons		24	30	34	26	28	35	29	27	22	19	22	27	26
monocotyledons		20	16	15	17	19	17	14	12	11	10	13	16	16
		63	64	76	66	67	73	66	62	51	53	59	64	66
Total Trophic Mean Score		81	85	74	91	85	88	85	77	80	72	73	78	74
Common Species Score		**68**	**79**	**73**	**92**	**88**	**75**	**69**	**72**	**86**	**69**	**69**	**74**	**65**

TABLE 4

RBSQ-C

Species	Trophic Rank	Ci	Cii	Ciii	C2i	C2ii	C2iii	C2iv	C2▲	C3i	C3ii	C3iii	C3iv	C3▲	C4i	C4ii	C4iii
Carex acuta	40	21														39	25
Cardamine amara	30	21		32												83	54
Equisetum palustre	58	53	21	24	32	58					55					100	88
Phalaris arundinacea	78	74	86	52	82	92	85	20	33	100	100	100	24		100	61	29
Myriophyllum alterniflorum	18	37	26	20	61	42	40	88	100	89	100	95	88	44	85	83	83
Veronica beccabunga	76	53	42	52	25	33	25	38	67	22	20	35		22	31	67	50
Carex nigra	14	53	37	32	25				20	22	36	30	53		23	94	88
Eleocharis palustris	56	47	58	64	71	50	30	31		56	64	55			92	100	75
Caltha palustris	54	100	79	72	64	67	25	77	67	100	81	85	53	22	77	94	96
Mentha aquatica	77	100	58	72	36	33	80	65	50	78	100	55	88	100	100	83	92
Myosotis scorpioides	62	58	21	72	46	50	60	38	100	100	64	50	71	56	100	100	83
Ranunculus flamula	26	21	100	100	96	100	55	81	83	78	82	100	71	100	54	94	96
Agrostis stolonifera	53	89	42	52	57	83	100	96	67	89	100	100	100	100	100	94	88
Glyceria fluitans	47	37	53	80	64	42	70	54	100	100	82	85	100	100	100		
Juncus effusus	51	42	37	20		33	65	77	83	100	100	85	88	100	69		
Callitriche stagnalis	143			44			65	42	83	44	20	80	65		77	39	46
Callitriche hamulata	23					75		69	33	67	82		65	78	77	28	63
Littorella uniflora	61				36		30	20	33	33	45	55			38		
Ranunculus penicillatus	69				29	42	20	27		22	20	50	29	67			
Apium nodiflorum	106											35	24	67			
Alisma plantago-aquatica	109					25				33	45	45		33			
Sparganium emersum	102					67	35			100		20					
Elodea canadensis	71				29		20			33	20	20	35				
Iris pseudocorus	60				29	33	30			44	73	25			31	33	
Lemna minor	139																
Apium inundatum	20									22	27			22	23		
Ranunculus fluitans	45								50						31		
Rorippa nasturtium-aquaticum	97			20			25				45		35			50	
Juncus bulbosus	44				36	50		23		33	45		29		38	33	75
Sparganium erectum	103					50	50		50	56	82	80	65		54	78	33
Carex aquatilis	12									100		20			31	22	21
Carex rostrata	22									78	45	20			46	61	67
Potamogeton natans	74									78	45	20			46	61	67
Equisetum fluviatile	57									89	27	40	35		38	44	42
Menyanthes trifoliata	52									33							

RBSQ-C	Trophic Rank	C1i	C1ii	C1iii	C2i	C2ii	C2iii	C2iv	C2v	C3i	C3ii	C3iii	C3iv	C3v	C4i	C4ii	C4iii
Potentilla palustris	28									33							
Scirpus fluitans	6									22							
Scirpus lacustris	142									22							
Nuphar lutea	138									44				22			
Ranunculus hederaceus	65												35				
Callitriche obtusangula	83													67			
Hydrocotyle vulgaris	59													33			
Ranunculus omiophyllus	19											35	41	78			
Ranunculus peltatus	48										20	20			31		
Polygonum amphibium	141														31		
Glyceria maxima	116													22	31	22	
Ranunculus aquatilis	70																
Carex acutiformis	110															28	
Potamogeton polygonifolius	4													56			25
algae		6	4	5	6	4	3	3	3	2	3	3	2	-	4	5	5
lichens		1	2	3	2	1	2	2	2	2	2	2	1	-	2	1	2
liverworts		5	6	8	7	8	7	6	6	4	5	6	5	3	6	4	6
mosses		15	14	19	11	11	12	15	15	13	14	8	10	4	6	4	15
vascular cryptogams		2	3	3	3	3	2	3	2	3	4	3	4	1	3	4	4
dicotyledons		16	21	25	19	24	28	22	21	27	28	30	25	32	28	28	26
monocotyledons		12	10	11	10	14	11	10	9	20	15	19	11	13	16	19	19
		57	60	74	58	65	65	61	58	71	71	71	58	53	69	76	77
Total Trophic Mean Score		49	57	52	63	72	68	55	46	61	59	62	67	66	62	59	53
Common Species Score		**65**	**69**	**54**	**61**	**63**	**51**	**48**	**52**	**50**	**54**	**66**	**56**	**65**	**60**	**57**	**45**

TABLE 5

RBSQ–D	Trophic Rank	D1i	D1ii	D2i	D3i	D3ii	D4i	D
Veronica beccabunga	76	32						
Sparganium erectum	103		33					
Caltha palustris	54	**92**	**83**	20	42		69	
Littorella uniflora	61	20	33				53	
Callitriche hamulata	23	52	**67**			35	**74**	
Myriophyllum alterniflorum	18	**68**	**67**			31	**84**	
Mentha aquatica	77	56	33		27		47	
Myosotis scorpioides	62	60	**67**		23	20	63	
Carex rostrata	22	60				23	**89**	
Equisetum fluviatile	57		50				**79**	
Equisetum palustre	58		25				32	
Veronica scutellata	26		25				27	
Phalaris arundinacea	78		58				37	
Sparganium emersum	102		25				21	
Callitriche stagnalis	143	52	33	20	23	20	37	
Ranunculus flammula	26	**100**	**83**	40	62	**77**	**89**	
Agrostis stolonifera	53	**100**	**100**	47	**92**	42	68	
Carex nigra	14	**96**	50	53	50	**69**	**95**	
Juncus bulbosus	44	**96**	**75**	**67**	58	**88**	**100**	
Juncus effusus	51	**88**	**92**	**67**	**96**	85	**95**	
Glyceria fluitans	47	**84**	**100**		**69**	46	**95**	
Potamogeton polygonifolius	4	24				62	63	
Ranunculus omiophyllus	19		25			31	32	
Hydrocotyle vulgaris	27						26	
Nuphar lutea	138						21	
Eleocharis palustris	56						**68**	
Iris pseudacorus	60						21	
Potamogeton natans	74						32	
Sparganium augustifolium	7						21	
algae		3	2	3	2	3	3	4
lichens		2	2	2	2	1	2	2
liverworts		8	6	7	6	5	6	8
mosses		21	20	21	13	13	18	22
vascular crytogams		2	4	1	2	1	4	4
dicotyledons		24	25	15	14	13	28	30
monocotyledons		17	15	14	12	19	25	31
		77	74	63	51	55	86	101
Total Trophic Mean Score		48	53	55	57	41	52	
Common Species Score		**38**	**42**	**48**	**50**	**34**	**39**	

3.   **DISCUSSION**

3.1   **Appraisal of Ranking System**

The community descriptions have clearly shown that the Trophic Ranks assigned by Newbold and Palmer are valuable in assessing the trophic status of riverine plant communities. By inference, therefore, they should be just as valuable in assessing the trophic status of most freshwater habitats.

To assess how accurately the Trophic Scores have objectively reflected the true picture of the prevailing trophic conditions in each of the 56 community types is difficult. It is considered that a true reflection has been given for more than 50 of the 56 end-groups and only five scores might be construed as anomolous.

To justify such confidence specific cases are considered below with reference to figure 2. At the same time the limitations of the system are also highlighted.

i)   The relatively low Trophic Score for community A1iii, characterised by rivers with enriched water and nutrient poor substrates, shows how the Trophic Score reflects how the substrate can mitigate against the influences of the water. If water analyses alone had been considered it is highly likely that these rivers would have shown a similar trophic status as others in sub-group A1. However because the substrates are nutrient poor sands the floral community has a less eutrophic expression.

ii)   The Trophic Scores of clay communities A2ii and A2v illustrate how floral assemblages can be classified as similar yet they can have very different trophic expressions. In the Report A2ii was described as anomolous because few sites were associated with clay yet the community was placed next to other communities associated with clay. The reason was that although most flowed on Permian and Triassic Sandstone and Mudstone, they contained some species typical of clay rivers. However investigating its trophic status by looking at its plant assemblages highlights how different this community is; it has a Trophic Score lower than all other Group A communities which places it on a par with the sandstone and limestone communities of Group B. A2v on the other hand has one of the highest Trophic Scores for any community because such assemblages are associated with nutrient rich clay substrates which are bathed in base-rich ground water.

iii) The high Trophic Score for classic Chalk rivers (A3i) compared with those suffering silt deposition (A3iii) was not expected. One explanation is that the very stable flow regime of the former favours some species with high Trophic Ranks because either their roots or shoots are constantly bathed in a fresh supply of bases and nutrients. An alternative explanation is that the reduction in species diversity (>25%) has someway affected the community balance. Even if this is accepted, it cannot be adequately argued that these rivers have a higher Trophic Status than a community of another Chalk river which is constantly being showered in rich silts.

iv) The relatively low Trophic Scores for the feeder streams and ditches of lowland rivers (A4) illustrate that although they flow on similar geological strata these watercoures are less likely to have accumulated an increase in Trophic Status from urban or agricultural run-off.

v) The Trophic Scores for A4 communities are in line with those expected for Group A, this showing that a relatively small number of species can be used to determine Trophic Scores. It might have been argued that the reduction in Trophic Scores from A1 to D4 might have been a function of the gradual reduction in the number of species used to calculate the Scores. However all Scores for A4i, ii, iii and iv are calculated on just seven or eight species and the mean score is over 80. Six community types in Group D had Trophic Scores calculated using at least seven species, and in the case of D4i there were 27 species used. Despite this the mean Trophic Score is only 42 and for D4i it is only 39.

vi) Three community types in Group B had Trophic Scores exceeding 85, well above the mean for the Group as a whole and comparable to some communities of Group A. The three communities of Group B with Trophic Scores differing widely from the mean were all described in the Report as more enriched by nutrients than other communities. This was stressed for the two communities of B2 since they are associated with the lower reaches of the R. Tweed and R. Eden which flow over rich geological strata. The high Trophic Score for winterbournes (B4iv) also illustrates how the use of the Trophic Ranks assigned by Newbold and Palmer can objectively evaluate the trophic characteristics of different communities to confirm previous subjective discriminations.

vii) The very low Trophic Score for C1iii compared with C1i and C1ii illustrates how effectively the Trophic Ranking System can even distinguish between the subtle differences in trophic status at the lower, oligo/mesotrophic end of the scale. In the Report it was noted that C1iii communities normally occurred on rich substrata but were fed by acid water draining peat-clad mountains. This community therefore occurs upstream of the other two communities and its predicted lower trophic status is objectively confirmed by it obtaining a Trophic Score more than 20% lower than the other two.

viii) The very low Trophic Score for upland rivers flowing through fen and bog (C3i) confirms that these communities have a genuine oligo-mesotrophic expression. The Trophic Score of only 50 was achieved from a community with as many as 32 taxa assigned Trophic Ranks. This shows that even at the oligotrophic end of the scale a large number of species recorded will still reflect the true trophic status of the habitats.

ix)   The Trophic Scores for the six community types in Group D illustrate that on a crude scale the system can highlight oligotrophic river communities; all have scores lower than those in Groups A-C. Differentation of the slight variations in the trophic status of these different oligotrophic communities is more difficult.   Although a true picture can be gained for community D4i because it contains 27 species allocated Ranks, such accuracy cannot be obtained for community D2i because only seven of the species present have been allocated Ranks. A realistically very low score is obtained in the former yet the latter, which is probably much more oligotrophic, has a higher score.   This is because there are no bryophytes allocated Trophic Ranks and the very sparse higher plant flora is dominated by tough, generalist, species which have average Trophic Ranks to express this.

x)   By an objective use of the Trophic Ranking system it has been possible to make a rough appraisal of the distribution within Great Britain of trophically rich and poor rivers.   These findings are summarised in Fig. 3.   What is interesting is that the system enables the most rich communities of Group B to manifest themselves as more enriched than some Group A communities.

3.2   Modifications and Improvements to the Trophic Ranking System

The way in which the system of Newbold and Palmer has been used here is not as primarily intended by them. In general it was envisaged that the trophic status of freshwater habitats would be evaluated by seeing how many species within a particular trophic range occurred within the site. Thus, if all the species at a site had low Ranks - then the site must be oligotrophic; if on the other hand the site included a number of plants with high Ranks - then the site must be eutrophic.

Rarely, however are communities so discrete, as shown here, and the authors were reticent to give the system objectivity because of the difficulty in testing it. This was completely understandable since the system was based on arbitrarily assigning a Rank to different species, each assignment affecting all the others. The completely unbiased use of the system here illustrates that it can be used objectively and in so doing can provide an accurate insight into the trophic status of different freshwater habitats.

The following suggestions may improve its use in other investigations into the trophic status of freshwater habitats.

i)   When using the Ranks 1-150 to calculate the mean Trophic Score for a habitat, it is recommended that some of the generalist species which span the complete trophic range are omitted. This is particularly important for oligotrophic sites. The species suggested for omission include: Glyceria fluitans, Agrostis stolonifera, Myosotis scorpioides, Mentha aquatica, Potamogeton crispus, Phragmites australis, Lemna minor, Callitriche stagnalis, Hippurus vulgaris, Fontinalis antipyretica, Rhynchostegium riparioides.

ii) Common bryophytes and algae might be assigned Trophic Ranks comparable to those of the higher plants. It is suggested that these dove-tail into the existing scale of 1-150, necessitating a similar Rank Number being used more than once. The following river algae are suggested: Hildenbrandia rivularis 55, Lemanea fluviatilis 51, Vaucheria 135, Enteromorpha 140, Cladophora 122.

The following common aquatic river bryophytes are suggested: Marsupella aquatica 5, Nardia compressa 5, Racomitrium aciculare 18, Pellia epiphylla 25, Scapania undulata 25, Hygropypnum ochraceum 20, Fontinalis squamosa 40, Amblystegium riparium 126.

Fontinalis antipyretica (56) and Rhynchostegium riparioides, (50), the commonest aquatic mosses, are included but since they span the complete trophic range they are not recommended for use in objective assessments.

iii) The use of species which are common in a particular habitat give the best results. This was illustrated for the river communities using species which occurred at high frequency within each community type. By inference it is thus more likely that the commoner species at any type of freshwater site are likely to more accurately reflect the trophic status of the site. Rarer species, however, may give an insight into subtle differences of soil type within micro-habitats such as bays or alcoves.

iv)   When equating the Trophic Ranks assigned to species by Newbold and Palmer to their distribution within British rivers, a number of taxa might be considered for Rank re-assessment. Reference to Table 6 shows that some species clearly appear to have trophic ranges in rivers which do not equate to our expectations throughout the complete spectrum of aquatic habitats.   This is hardly surprising since many riverine habitats are very specialised and determining the primary factors which determine whether a species might be present or absent are difficult to unravel.   The case of Littorella uniflora illustrates this since in rivers it is confined to shingle in fast-flowing sections where the trophic status of the substrate and water are low.   It thus has an affinity to water courses with a low trophic status yet it is capable of growing on the shores of base-rich lakes.   Any re-allocation of ranks should thus be done with considerable care since it is possible that the distribution of some species in rivers is related to physical constraints which might lead to spurious trophic interpretation. Myosoton aquaticum however has been clearly allocated a Rank too low, as has Ranunculus fluitans.   The Ranunculus can withstand eutrophic water, but not pollution, so an increase from 45 to 60 is recommended.   Myosoton occurs most commonly on clay substrates and a doubling of its Rank from 37 to 74 is proposed.   Both Veronica catenata and V. anagallis-aquatica have been allocated Ranks too low and these have been increased to 105 and 106 respectively.

v)   The above amendments to the system, showing only those species which are likely to be encountered in rivers, are shown in Table 6.   This Table also incorporates an appraisal of the trophic responses of these plants in rivers compared with their responses in other wetland habitats.

vi)   The assignment of Ranks to species by Newbold and Palmer was based primarily on an analysis of pH, conductivity and alkalinity data in combination with their field experience supplemented by information given in Clapham, Tutin and Warburg (1962).   For the species included in this document it would be desirable to obtain nutrient data from Water Authorities to either confirm their correct position within the Ranking System or to aid in their regrading.

3.3   Validation of Suggested Modifications

Figure 4 compares the Trophic Scores calculated for 14 community types.   The closed symbols indicate the scores derived from the unmodified Trophic Ranking System and the open symbols indicate the scores for comparable communities using the system with the modifications suggested above.

At the eutrophic end of the system the modifications make relatively little difference (as intended) although most of these enriched communities show slightly higher Trophic Scores.   The amendments to the system do, however, have a great effect at the oligotrophic end.   The main concern expressed in 2.4 about the inability of the unmodified system to reflect accurately true oligotrophic communities are now overcome.   Considerable concern was expressed that the high scores for D2ii and D3i did not reflect that these communities should have lower scores than D1i and D2i. The simple modifications to the system, however, enable its objective use to illustrate that the rocky communities of D2ii and D3i are indeed of a lower trophic status than those of D1i and D2i. The particularly low Score for D3ii further illustrates the importance of not using ubiquitous species.

3.4 Value of Ranking System in Monitoring and Nature Conservation Evaluation

Because of the points illustrated previously it is strongly urged that the objective Ranking System is used in assessments of a variety of freshwater habitats for conservation purposes. It may also prove a most valuable monitoring tool to ascertain if changes in the nutrient status of previously well documented sites is indeed occurring.

Methods to cater adequately for both these practical applications might need slight development but however approached both illustrate the great value of macrophytes in this field. Macrophytes have relatively few representatives, they are recorded easily, they do not move (and therefore reflect conditions over very long periods) and they have been shown repeatedly to be fundamental to the success of balanced and diverse animal communities in both flowing and standing waters. For long-term monitoring they also have the advantage of being actively recorded and collected, herbarium specimens often being available to substantiate written accounts.

This document should be regarded only as a discussion paper to illustrate the scope of a macrophyte trophic ranking system in freshwater evaluations. For this reason there have been few references to published work by others. If there is sufficient response from it, it would be desirable to obtain detailed chemical data concerning the substrates and sediments of rivers from relevant sources within the water industry. These should be then equated to the known distribution of plants in rivers; our own data should be suplemented by that held by Haslam, the Freshwater Biological Association, Institute of Terrestrial Ecology, Universities and other institutes involved in such work.

REFERENCES

Clapham A.R., Tutin T.G. and Warburg E.F. (1962) Flora of the British Isles. CUP, London.

Haslam S.M. (1978) River Plants. 396pp. CUP, London.

Holmes N.T.H. (1983) Typing British Rivers According to their Flora. Focus on Nature Conservation No. 4. NCC, London.

Newbold C. and Palmer M. (1979) Trophic Adaptions of Aquatic Plants. CST Note No 18. Internal Report, NCC, London.

Fig. 3 Map showing Trophic Status of rivers in Great Britain.

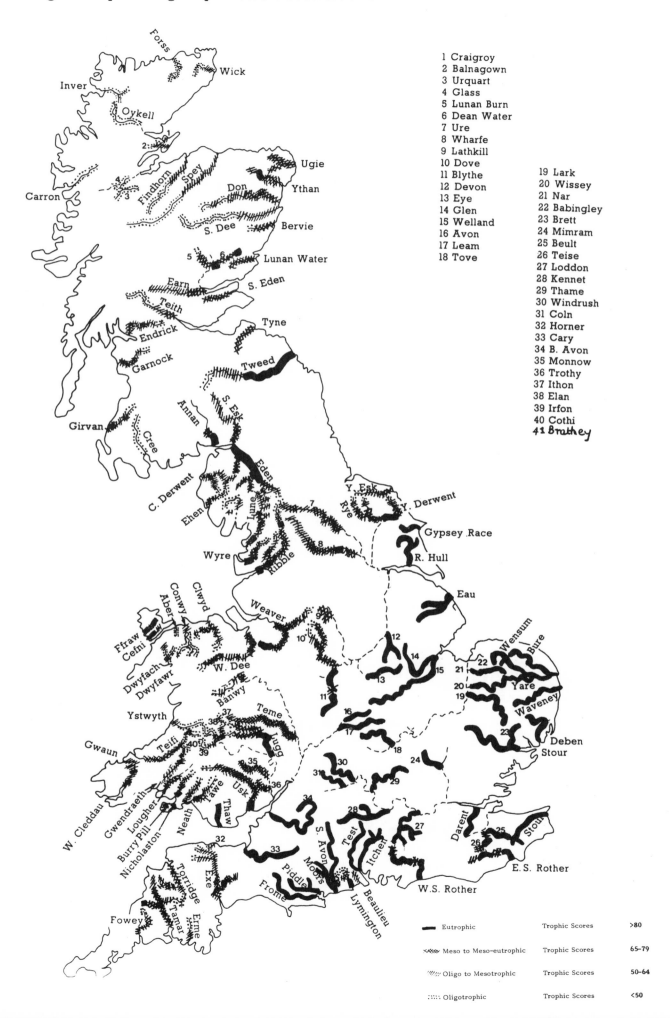

1 Craigroy
2 Balnagown
3 Urquart
4 Glass
5 Lunan Burn
6 Dean Water
7 Ure
8 Wharfe
9 Lathkill
10 Dove
11 Blythe
12 Devon
13 Eye
14 Glen
15 Welland
16 Avon
17 Leam
18 Tove

19 Lark
20 Wissey
21 Nar
22 Babingley
23 Brett
24 Mimram
25 Beult
26 Teise
27 Loddon
28 Kennet
29 Thame
30 Windrush
31 Coln
32 Horner
33 Cary
34 B. Avon
35 Monnow
36 Trothy
37 Ithon
38 Elan
39 Irfon
40 Cothi
41 Brathey

▬ Eutrophic	Trophic Scores	>80
⨯⨯⨯ Meso to Meso-eutrophic	Trophic Scores	65–79
///// Oligo to Mesotrophic	Trophic Scores	50–64
:::::: Oligotrophic	Trophic Scores	<50

48

Fig 4. Appraisal of recommended amendments to the Trophic Ranking System; (.) indicate **Trophic Scores** calculated using the original system and **(X)** show the Trophic Scores derived from the amended system. Small differences are evident at the eutrophic end **(A)** but large reductions in Score occur at the oligotrophic end **(D)**.

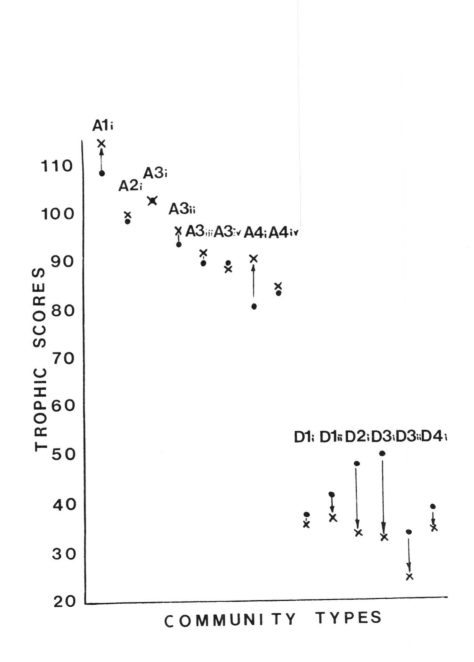

TABLE 6

This Table summarises information on the trophic expression of individual plant species in rivers in comparison to their trophic response in all water types.   The bold lines and blocks show the presence of species within each of the 16 sub-groups whilst the dotted lines duplicate the trophic ranges shown by Newbold and Palmer in CST Note 18.   Although not strictly accurate (see Text) for ease of comparison the sub-groups D1-4 are coded as oligotrophic; sub-groups C2, 3 and 4 as oligo-mesotrophic; C4, B3 and B4 as mesotrophic; B1 and B2 as meso-eutrophic and A1-4 as eutrophic.

The Table also shows the additions to the Ranking system recommended in 3.2 as well as the recommended new Rank Numbers (   ) and the species not recommended for calculation of Trophic Scores **X**.

=	distribution in river sub-groups exceeds 50%	
=	occurrence in river sub-groups normally between 20-50%	
=	usual distribution in all water types	(Data duplicated (from
=	occurring uncommonly in all water types	(Newbold & Palmer

TABLE 6

TROPHIC RANK	SPECIES	Trophic type given by Newbold and Palmer 16 sub-groups	OLIGOTROPHIC				OLIGO/MESOTROPHIC				MESOTROPHIC				MESO/EUTROPHIC			EUTROPHIC
			D4	D3	D2	D1	C4	C3	C2	C1	B4	B3	B2	B1	A4	A3	A2	A1
4	Potamogeton polygonifolius (Bog Pondweed)																	
5	Nardia compressa																	
5	Marsupella emarginata																	
6	Scirpus fluitans (Floating Club-rush)																	
7	Sparganium angustifolium (Floating Bur-reed)																	
12	Carex aquatilis (Water Sedge)																	
14	Carex nigra (Common Sedge)																	
18	Myriophyllum alterniflorum (Alternate Water-milfoil)																	
18	Racomitrium aciculare																	
19	Ranunculus omiophyllus (Round-leaved Crowfoot)																	
20	Apium inundatum (Less Marshwort)																	
20	Hygrohypnum ochraceum (Lesser Marshwort)																	
22	Carex rostrata (Bottle Sedge)																	
23	Callitriche hamulata (Intermediate starwort)																	
25	Scapania undulata																	
25	Pellia epiphylla																	
26	Ranunculus flammula (Lesser Spearwort)																	
27	Veronica scutellata (Marsh Speedwell)																	
28	Potentilla palustris (Marsh Cinquefoil)																	
30	Cardamine amara (Large Bitter-cress)																	

TABLE 6 (2)

			OLIGOTROPHIC				OLIGO-MESOTROPHIC				MESOTROPHIC				MESO-EUTROPHIC				EUTROPHIC

TROPHIC RANK

Trophic type given by Newbold and Palmer

species	16 sub-groups	D4 D3 D2 D1	C4 C3 C2 C1	B4 B3 B2 B1	A4 A3 A2 A1

Trophic Rank	Species	
37 (74)	Myosoton aquaticum (Water Chickweed)	
40	Fontinalis squamosa	
40	Carex acuta (Slender Tufted-sedge)	
42	Glyceria plicata (Plicate Sweet-grass)	
44	Juncus bulbosus (Bulbous Rush)	
45 (60)	Ranunculus fluitans (River Water-crowfoot)	
X47	Glyceria fluitans (Floating Sweet-grass)	
X48	Ranunculus peltatus (Pond Water-crowfoot)	
X50	Rhynchostegium riparioides	
51	Lemanea fluviatilis	
51	Juncus effusus (Soft Rush)	
52	Menyanthes trifoliata (Bog bean)	
X53	Agrostis stolonifera (Creeping Bent)	
54	Caltha palustris (Marsh-marigold)	
55	Hildenbrandia rivularis	
56	Eleocharis palustris (Common Spike-rush)	
X56	Fontinalis antipyretica	
57	Equisetum fluviatile (Water Horsetail)	

TABLE 6 (3)

TROPHIC RANK	species	Trophic type given by Newbold and Palmer / 16 sub-groups	OLIGOTROPHIC				OLIG-MESOTROPHIC				MESOTROPHIC				MESO-EUTROPHIC				EUTROPHIC
			D4	D3	D2	D1	C4	C3	C2	C1	B4	B3	B2	B1	A4	A3	A2	A1
58	Equisetum palustre (Marsh Horsetail)																	
59	Hydrocotyle vulgaris (Marsh Pennywort)																	
60 (41)	Iris pseudacorus (Yellow Iris)																	
61	Littorella uniflora (Shoreweed)																	
X62	Myosotis scorpioides (Water Forget-me-not)																	
64	Potamogeton gramineus (Various-leaved Pondweed)																	
65	Ranunculus hederaceus (Ivy-leaved Crowfoot)																	
66	Veronica anagallis-aquatica (Blue Water-speedwell)																	
67	Veronica catenata (Pink Water-speedwell)																	
69	Ranunculus penicillatus (Stream Water-crowfoot)																	
70	Ranunculus aquatilis (Common Water-crowfoot)																	
71	Elodea canadensis (Canadian Waterweed)																	
72	Elodea nuttallii (Nuttall's Waterweed)																	
73	Potamogeton alpinus (Reddish Pondweed)																	
74	Potamogeton natans (Broad-leaved Pondweed)																	
75	Ranunculus trichophyllus (Thread-leaved Water-crowfoot)																	

TABLE 6 (4)

TROPHIC RANK	species	Trophic type given by Newbold and Palmer — 16 sub-groups	OLIGOTROPHIC		OLIGO-MESOTROPHIC			MESOTROPHIC			MESO-EUTROPHIC			EUTROPHIC	
			D4 D3	D2 D1	C4 C3	C2 C1	B4	B3 B2	B1	A4	A3 A2	A1			

- 76 — Veronica beccabunga (Brooklime)
- X77 — Mentha aquatica (Water mint)
- 78 — Phalaris arundinacea (Reed Canary grass)
- 80 — Azolla filiculoides (Water Fern)
- 81 — Berula erecta (Lesser Water-parsnip)
- 82 — Butomus umbellatus (Flowering Rush)
- 83 — Callitriche obtusangula (Blunt-fruited Water-starwort)
- 86 — Catabrosa aquatica (Whorl-grass)
- 88 — Lemna gibba (Fat Duckweed)
- 89 — Lemna trisulca (Ivy-leaved Duckweed)
- 92 — Potamogeton berchtoldii (Small Pondweed)
- 95 — Potamogeton pusillus (Lesser Pondweed)
- 97 — Nasturtium microphyllum/officinale (Watercress)
- 98 — Ranunculus circinatus (Fan-leaved Water-crowfoot)
- 99 — Ranunculus calcareus (Brook Water-crowfoot)
- 100 — Rumex hydrolapathum (Water Dock)
- 102 — Sparganium emersum (Unbranched Bur-reed)

TABLE 6 (5)

TROPHIC RANK	Trophic type given by Newbold and Palmer	OLIGOTROPHIC	OLIG-MESOTROPHIC	MESOTROPHIC	MESO-EUTROPHIC	EUTROPHIC
species	16 sub-groups	D4 D3 D2 D1	C4 C3 C2 C1	B4 B3 B2 B1	A4 A3 A2 A1	

103 Sparganium erectum (Branched Bur-reed)

106 Apium nodiflorum (Fool's Water-cress)

107 Oenanthe fluviatilis (River Water-dropwort)

108 Alisma lanceolatum (Narrow-leaved Water-plantain)

109 Alisma plantago-aquatica (Water-plantain)

110 Carex acutiformis (Less Pond-sedge)

111 Ranunculus sceleratus (Celery-leaved Buttercup)

112 Rorippa amphibia (Great Yellow-cress)

112 Cladophora glomerata

113 Carex paniculata (Great Tussock Sedge)

114 Carex riparia (Great Pond-sedge)

116 Glyceria maxima (Reed Sweet-grass)

117 Groenlandia densa (Opposite-leaved Pondweed)

124 Potamogeton lucens (Shining Pondweed)

126 Amblystegium riparium

127 Sagittaria sagittifolia (Arrowhead)

128 Scirpus martimus (Sea Club-rush)

135 Potamogeton perfoliatus (Perfoliate Pondweed)

TABLE 6 (6)

TROPHIC RANK	species	Trophic type given by Newbold and Palmer 16 sub-groups	OLIGOTROPHIC				OLIG-MESOTROPHIC				MESOTROPHIC				MESO-EUTROPHIC				EUTROPHIC	
			D4	D3	D2	D1	C4	C3	C2	C1	B4	B3	B2	B1	A4	A3	A2	A1
135	Vaucheria spp.																	
X136	Enteromorpha spp.																	
137	Potamogeton crispus (Curly Pondweed)																	
138	Nuphar lutea (Yellow Water-lily)																	
X139	Lemna minor (Common Duckweed)																	
X140	Phragmites australis (Common Reed)																	
141	Polygonum amphibium (Amphibious Bistort)																	
142	Scirpus lacustris (Common Club-rush)																	
X143	Callitriche stagnalis (Common Water-starwort)																	
144	Ceratophyllum demersum (Rigid Hornwort)																	
146	Typha latifolia (Bulrush)																	
X147	Hippuris vulgaris (Mare's Tail)																	
148	Myriophyllum spicatum (Spiked Water-milfoil)																	
149	Potamogeton pectinatus (Fennel Pondweed)																	
150	Zannichellia palustris (Horned Pondweed)																	

APPENDIX

A summary of the characteristics of the main communities, and their distribution, is duplicated from **Focus on Nature Conservation No 4.**

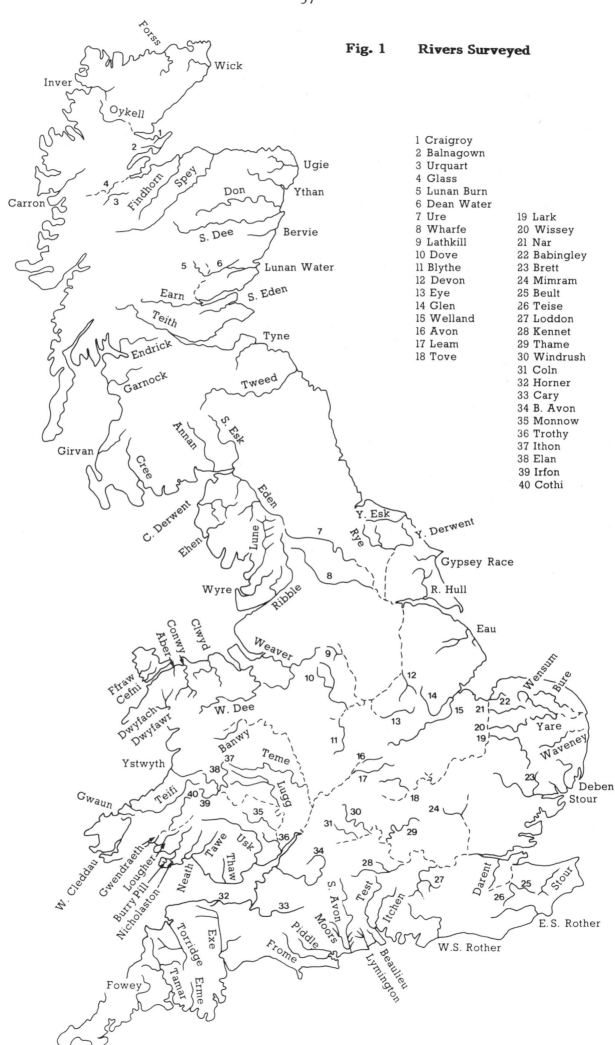

Fig. 1   Rivers Surveyed

1 Craigroy
2 Balnagown
3 Urquart
4 Glass
5 Lunan Burn
6 Dean Water
7 Ure
8 Wharfe
9 Lathkill
10 Dove
11 Blythe
12 Devon
13 Eye
14 Glen
15 Welland
16 Avon
17 Leam
18 Tove
19 Lark
20 Wissey
21 Nar
22 Babingley
23 Brett
24 Mimram
25 Beult
26 Teise
27 Loddon
28 Kennet
29 Thame
30 Windrush
31 Coln
32 Horner
33 Cary
34 B. Avon
35 Monnow
36 Trothy
37 Ithon
38 Elan
39 Irfon
40 Cothi

Fig. 2　Distribution of main Groups
A, B, C and D

● Group A: Lowland and Rich Geology
■ Group B: Sandstone, Millstone & Hard Limestone
▲ Group C: Resistant Geology
◆ Group D: Upland Acid & Nutrient Poor

GROUP A COMMUNITIES (RBSQ)

This group is the largest of the four major groups and contains 386 sites. All of these sites are either base-rich or nutrient rich, and usually both. They occur exclusively at low altitudes and usually where the slope of the river is very shallow. They can, therefore, be described as lowland and nutrient rich communities.

Geographical distribution

This group is typified by communities in central, southern and eastern England south-east of a line drawn roughly from Scarborough to Exeter. A narrow flange in the midlands fans west from this line to include the rivers in the lowland plains of Cheshire and Staffordshire. Further north, the flood plains of central Yorkshire also contain lowland communities.

The rivers of the New Forest are the only examples in southern England of rivers with communities which are consistently not clasified within this group. Apart from these rivers, the R. Teise, and the W.S. Rother are the only examples of rivers which have two of their sites not within Group A. The uppermost sites of the E.S. Rother, Lambourne, Moors, Uddens and B. Avon are the only other examples of sites within this geographical area which are not classified as Group A communities.

Of the 386 sites in Group A, 10 occur in Wales remote from the centre of its range (4 on Anglesey, 1 on the W. Cleddau, 1 on the Lougher, 2 on the Nicholaston Pill and 2 on the Thaw). Seven occur similarly in Scotland (1 on the Wick, 2 on the Ythan, 2 on the Dean, 1 on the Teith and 1 on the Tweed). There is only one example in England (R. Inny) distant from the representative geographical area. The remaining 368 sites (95%) occur within, or on the edge of, the defined geographical area. Within this area, 94% of the sites are classified as having Group A communities and the streams of the New Forest account for half of the atypical classifications.

Excluding the New Forest, therefore, 97% of rivers in central, southern and eastern England have a distinct Group A plant community. The area of Group A can therefore be defined as lowland England, excluding the streams of acid heaths and sands. Almost all the area is below 200m with only the summits of named Wolds, Downs and Hills exceeding this height.

Geology

The geology is characterised by the lack of any resistant rock. The Chalk of Great Britain is confined to this area, as are the majority of the harder and less pure Oolites. Clays account for almost 50% of the area with alluvium and peat important on the east coast and in East Anglia. Soft sands are important components in the Cheshire Plain, in the Vales of the Yorkshire Ouse and Trent, in East Anglia, the edges of the Weald and in the New Forest area.

In general, the geology of this central, southern and eastern region of England is characterised by rocks which are rich in either nutrients or bases, or rich in both. The sands of the New Forest and on the edge of the Weald are the major exceptions, both having few nutrients and being poor in bases.

Physical characteristics and variations

Rivers in central England are typified by fine substrates of clay or silt over which the water flows with only slow or moderate velocity. These two characteristics of the rivers are a function of their sources being at low altitudes and their channels passing over soft deposits which are easily eroded into fine substrates.

There are three clearly distinct substrates which result from the very different parent rock types.

The most distinct is the coarse gravels, pebbles and even cobbles which are a feature of the streams and rivers flowing over Chalk. Because these rivers receive the majority of water from underground sources, their flow capacity varies little through the seasons. The water is characteristically crystal clear with siltation confined to their lowermost reaches or in backwaters or sheltered alcoves at the edges of the water courses. The Rivers Test and Itchen in Hampshire epitomise the characteristics of Chalk rivers whereas the middle reaches of the R. Nar in Norfolk and the Upper Kelk Beck and R. Hull in Humberside are typical of smaller Chalk streams. Rivers flowing over Oolite have some features akin to those which flow over Chalk yet they generally rise at much higher altitudes and then carry inflated volumes of water after heavy rain. The Rivers Coln and Windrush in the Cotswold are typical examples, both of which have much coarser substrates in their upper reaches.

Fine sandy substrates, occasionally accompanied by gravels, are a characteristic feature of rivers flowing over the soft sandstones of Cheshire, the Vales of the Yorkshire Ouse and Trent and the smaller rivers in Norfolk. The sandstones in southern England, and especially those of the New Forest, are generally base poor. Because of their open texture water flows rapidly through these rocks and the rivers which they produce frequently rise and fall rapidly and have coarse gravels and pebbles as typical substrates. They are frequently erosive channels.

The rivers which flow over clay are characterised by very fine sediments or clay itself. Flow velocity is generally slow during low flows. A major feature of clay rivers is their behaviour after heavy rain. Since clay is impervious, rain drains rapidly into drainage channels and river levels may rise dramatically, a 5m rise in the largest rivers being possible. In contrast, during very dry weather the levels drop very low.

Vegetation characteristics of Group A communities

Lowland rivers are dominated by flowering plants and these communities also contain many more aquatic species than other river types. For instance Tables 4-7 show the relative importance of aquatic taxa in Groups A, B, C and D with Group A having 43 representatives, almost double the number found in Group B and C and quadruple the number found in Group D. Table 3 shows the important taxa for the 16 major subgroups and this also illustrates the importance of Group A for aquatic higher plants. Sixteen aquatic species are confined to being important components of Group A whereas the comparable numbers for Group B, C and D are 2, 0 and 2 respectively.

Concomitant with the greatest importance of aquatic flowering plants in Group A is the least importance of lower plants such as liverworts and mosses. This too is amply illustrated in Table 3 which lists 35 bryophytes, 75% of which are not represented in Group A. Table 8 further highlights this by showing that the combined bryophyte total for Group A river communities represents only 10% of the total species complement whereas the flowering plants represent 81%. The former is much lower than in any of the other three major groups and the latter is much higher.

The characteristic species of lowland rivers is most easily illustrated by reference to the top of Table 3. This shows the species confined to being important components of lowland rivers only.

Since Group A contains 21 community types it is important to discriminate between the four main sub-groups A1 to A4.

Group A1 is characteristic of rivers with calcareous water, often partially derived from Chalk aquifers, which flow through very flat country which ensures a slow water velocity. Substrates usually comprise of silts, sands and very fine gravels. The catchments are usually intensively farmed and there is considerable nutrient enrichment. The characteristic species are therefore submerged taxa which prefer sluggish water and a high level of nutrients. Shallow rooted or free floating species, as well as those taxa which prefer to receive nutrients from the water rather than the sediments, reach their greatest importance in this group.

Group A2 are clay rivers. Wherever clay is the major geological constituent of a catchment the flora will be dominated by species characteristic of Group A. Clay catchments usually provide an abundance of nutrients and fine sediments to a river. However, because the rivers rise and fall rapidly siltation is confined to stretches of water protected from the full force of flood water. An unmanaged clay river will thus provide a combination of firm rich substrates into which plants can root as well as more unstable fine silts in sheltered backwaters.

Group A3 are Chalk or Oolite rivers. All rivers with this community type share two important characteristics which are not found in other lowland rivers. Firstly, their primary source of water is from aquifers which provide a very stable flow regime, differences between minimum flows and peak floods being small. This provides a stable flow regime which assist colonization on the stream bed as well as maintaining a high water table on the bank. Secondly, gravels and other coarse substrates prevail.

Group A4 is a strange community which is dominated by the most upstream sites on lowland rivers which have ditch-like characteristics. They are highly managed, narrow rivers with steep sides and impoverished physical diversity. They differ, of course, from the true 'ditch' in having a large fluctuation in water level and an almost continuous, uni-directional flow of water through them.

Table 9 shows the distribution of Group A communities in the classification of rivers. The majority of sites are centred at the top of the Table which describes rivers which rise at altitudes lower than 200 metres. However, a striking feature of the communities associated with lowland rivers is that Group A communities are only associated with calcareous, eutrophic waters. The lowland rivers with non-calcareous rocks and oligotrophic or mesotrophic water rarely have these community types.

The sites surveyed in the rivers classified in the uppermost five boxes in Table 9 ie. lowland, meso-eutrophic and/or calcareous have 97% of their sites classified as Group A communities. On the other hand, lowland rivers classified as less calcareous and having less nutrient and base-rich water have less than 15% of their sites classified as having Group A communities.

Throughout the remainder of the classification which deals with rivers with altitudinal sources greater than 200 metres, Group A communities are rare. Throughout this part of the classification Group A communities represent a mere 5% of the total. In all but one example the sites are confined to the lower, more enriched sections of rivers. Moreover, almost 50% of the examples are confined to two rivers, the R. Coln and R. Windrush. These two rivers are the most calcareous examples because they drain the Oolite of the Cotswolds.

The classification also highlights several other points. Firstly, Group A3 communities are associated almost entirely with catchments dominated by Chalk or other soft limestones. Secondly, Group A4 communities invariably occur in the upper reaches of a river where the greatest effects of channel modification manifest themselves in the flora. Thirdly, Group A2 communities prevail in eutrophic, lowland rivers with no soft limestone in their catchments. These are usually dominated by clay. These points are further illustrated by reference to Fig. 3 but all serve to show that the classification of rivers based primarily on geology, altitude and trophic status is a valuable aid in ellucidating the patterns of river plant communities.

GROUP B COMMUNITIES (RBSQ)

This Group of 270 sites can be described as having meso-eutrophic plant communities which are primarily associated with sandstone and Carboniferous Limestone. The trophic status, and the community, of Group B is intermediate between the truly mesotrophic communities of Group C and the substantially more enriched communities of Group A.

Geographical distribution

Group B communities are highly correlated with the distribution in the British Isles of Devonian, Carboniferous, Permian and Triassic sediments. Where rivers rise at high altitudes, or where peat nullifies the richer elements of the sandstones and limestones, Group C communities are more likely to be found as both the sediments and the water are more oligotrophic. On the other hand, in the very eutrophicated rivers which flow over flat areas of New Red Sandstone, the expected community type will be Group A.

Group B communities thus range from south-west England where Devonian, Carboniferous and Permian deposits occur, to north-east Scotland where Old Red Sandstone and sandy metamorphic substrates with rich drift deposits predominate. Between these two geographical extremes are the extensive areas of Lower Old Red Sandstone of South Wales, Herefordshire and Worcestershire, the extensive New Red Sandstone and Carboniferous deposits of the Pennines and Lancashire, the Carboniferous Limestone and New Red Sandstone of north-east Lakeland, and the combination of these formations which stretch from Northumberland to Aberdeenshire in eastern Scotland.

The distribution of these geological features in Britain is mirrored by the distribution of Group B communities shown in Fig. 4.

Perhaps more noteworthy are the occurrences of Group B communities on rivers which traverse isolated pockets of Carboniferous Limestone or sandstone. For instance, the Rivers Esk, Annan and Girvan in south-west Scotland traverse sandstone in their lowermost reaches and when they do their community changes from Group C to Group B. No other major community Group is so closely allied to two geological formations as Group B is.

The four main sub-groups of B are both geographically and geologically discrete. Group B1 is characteristic of Scotland, Group B2 is characteristic of northern England and southern Scotland, Group B3 is closely correlated with very rich and soft sandstones and limestones and Group B4 communities occur most commonly in west Wales, south-west England and north-west England where high rainfall and less calcium rich substrates occur. Group A is the most geographically distinct and therefore its relationship between other Group B communities is impossible to assess. On the other hand there is a clear relationship between Groups B2–B4 in relation to stream size and trophic status. Group B4 is the most mesotrophic and invariably occurs upstream of Group B3. Only in extremely nutrient poor sandstone rivers is this community found in the lower reaches. Group B2 communities are associated with very large rivers and are likely to occur downstream of B3 or B4 communities.

National Variation

The classification of rivers (Table 9) shows that the majority of Group B communities occur on rivers which rise above 200m. However, within this broad category, Group B communities occur most frequently in catchments where sandstone and limestone are present. Only rarely are Group B communities found in catchments where resistant rock prevails.

These points are illustrated best by reference to specific points in the classification. For example, rivers included in the category-source >500m, resistant rock, oligotrophic, have only a single site (<2% of the total) classified in Group B. On the other hand rivers which rise at similar altitudes but flowing over limestone or sandstone and with eutrophic water have 25 sites (57% of the total) in Group B.

Because Group B communities are more enriched than those of Group C, but less so than Group A, these communities may be expected to occur in the middle reaches of large rivers which show classic downstream successional changes. There are, however, few good examples, the R. Dee in Wales and the R. Wharfe in Yorkshire being two of the best. What normally happens is that Group B communities do occur downstream of Group C communities but these communities remain throughout the length of the river. It is only when the river traverses extensive lowland flood plains or becomes polluted that Group A communities are found.

Vegetation characteristics of Group B communities

Table 3 shows which taxa are most important in Group B in relation to the other three major Groups of vegetation types and Table 5 shows the characteristic species of the sub-group communities of Groups B1-4.

The former Table clearly shows the affinity of Group B to Group A with the presence of many species characteristic of lowlands and enriched water. Typical aquatic examples include Lemna minor (Common Duckweed), Zannichellia palustris (Horned Pondweed) and Potamogeton pectinatus (Fennel Pondweed) which occur in Groups B1 and B2 and Ranunculus calcareus (Brook Water-crowfoot), Elodea canadensis (Canadian Pondweed) and Potamogeton crispus (Curly Pondweed) which occur in all B1-B4 Groups. The pollution tolerant moss Amblystegium riparium and the algae Enteromorpha and Cladophora glomerata are either confined to Groups A and B or only abundant in them.

Few taxa are confined to Group B alone but many are characteristic of the sandstones and limestones associated with the Group. Apart from the seven species shown in Table 3 to be allied solely to Group B, the red encrusting alga Hildenbrandia rivularis, the River Water-crowfoot (Ranunculus fluitans) and the Perfoliate Pondweed (Potamogeton perfoliatus) are aquatic species most associated with, but not confined to, Group B. On the banks, Rorippa palustris (Marsh Yellow-cress), R. sylvestris (Creeping Yellow-cress), Petasites hybridus (Butterbur), Impatiens glandulifera (Indian Balsam) and Mimulus guttatus (Monkey-flower) thrive on the sandy well drained banks.

The closely associated Collema fluviatile, Britain's largest purely aquatic lichen, and Cladophora aegagropila, a tough pelt-forming alga, are confined to Group B and are most characteristic of large sandstone or hard limestone pavements. The former was previously thought to be a nationally rare species confined to Tayside and the latter is an interesting species because it also grows in Tarns where wave-action causes it to grow into balls.

GROUP C COMMUNITIES (RBSQ)

This Group of 276 sites can be described as having an oligo-mesotrophic/mesotrophic status due to flowing over resistant rocks. Old rocks of the Silurian and Ordivician, together with the extensive areas with intrusive or extrusive rocks, are typical. In areas where sandstone is particularly hard and where high rainfall is combined with rocks low in nutrients and bases, Group C communities will also be found. Group C communities are not found above 300m (1,000 feet) but it would be very unusual if any rivers rising above this height did not have one or more Group C communities in its downstream succession.

Geographical distribution

Group C communities will be found most typically in south-west England, throughout Wales except in the south-east, the Lake District, North York Moors and throughout Scotland except in the geologically rich east or in the north-west where blanket bogs create true oligotrophic conditions. Group C communities are also common on the acid Tertiary sands of the New Forest and in some Pennines rivers where blanket bog in the catchment neutralizes the richness of the underlying geology.

National variation

Table 9 shows that every river surveyed which have their sources above 500m have Group C communities present. Oligotrophic rivers which flow on resistant rock usually have up to 50 km of their upper reaches as Group D but downstream succession results in Group C communities being present as the river approaches the sea. On sandstone or limestone rivers rising at high altitudes, only the uppermost few kilometres are sufficiently oligotrophic for Group D communities to occur. These are quickly succeeded downstream by Group C communities which are in turn succeeded by Group B communities in their lower reaches. Even rivers which rise at much lower altitudes, but flow entirely on resistant rock, have only Group D and then Group C communities. On limestone or sandstone however, or where rivers on resistant rock become eutrophic, Group C communities give way downstream to Group B, or even Group A, communities.

The R. Findhorn and the R. Dee in Scotland are thus prime examples of oligo-mesotrophic large rivers rising at high altitudes, the R. Conway in Wales, or the Brathay in England or the R. Cree and R. Spey in Scotland being similar examples for rivers rising at intermediate altitudes, whilst the R. Forss in Scotland is the best example in the lowland category. In the naturally mesotrophic to meso-eutrophic category the R. Teifi in Wales, the R. Ure in England and the R. Don in Scotland are good examples of rivers rising at high altitudes; the R. Ithon in Wales, the R. Exe in England and the R. Tweed in Scotland are good examples of rivers rising at intermediate altitudes whereas rivers rising at lower altitudes are represented by the R. North Ugie in Scotland, the Western Cleddau in Wales and the R.Torridge in England.

All the above examples have significant sections of river with Group C communities. At high altitudes the Group C sections of rivers are generally downstream of Group D communities. However at lower altitudes many of the rivers rise having Group C communities and downstream there is a succession to Group B communities. The Western Cleddau in Wales is a very unusual example because it becomes progressively more oligotrophic on passing downstream. This is because it rises on a flat river flood plain on clay and then traverses progressively coarser substrates. The river communities therefore rise as Group A, pass to Group B and remain consistently in Group C in the lower reaches.

Vegetation characteristics of Group C communities

Table 8 shows that the 141 taxa represented commonly in at least one sub-group of Group C spans a wide variety of plant types with 9 algae, 3 lichens, 8 liverworts, 23 mosses, 4 vascular cryptogams, 57 dicotyledons and 37 monocotyledons represented. The high numbers of dicotyledons is similar to the numbers in Group B but mosses are almost twice as important in Group C as they are in Group B.

The decrease in trophic status from Group B to Group C is best illustrated in Table 3. This shows that many taxa which are more typical of nutrient or base rich water are much less abundant in Group C than Group B, or absent from Group C altogether. Examples include Cladophora glomerata, Enteromorpha spp, Pellia endiviifolia, Amblystegium riparium, Apium nodiflorum (Fool's Water-cress), Callitriche platycarpa (Various leaved Water-starwort), Epilobium hirsutum (Great Willowherb), Myriophyllum spicatum (Spiked Water-milfoil), Ranunculus calcareus (Brook Water-crowfoot), Scrophularia auriculata (Water Figwort), Symphytum officinale (Comfrey), Elodea canadensis (Canadian Pondweed), Potamogeton crispus (Curly Pondweed), and many more. Conversely many taxa are more common in Group C than in Group B, or are represented in the Table for the first time because of the decrease in trophic status. Pellia epiphylla, Scapania undulata and Solenostoma triste are three such liverworts, Brachythecium plumosum, Dichodontium pellucidium, Hygrohypnum ochraceum and Racomitrium aciculare are four of many such mosses and Achillea ptarmica (Sneezewort), Ranunculus flammula (Lesser Spearwort) and Myriophyllum alterniflorum (Alternate-flowered Water-milfoil) are examples of higher plants.

Since there are 16 community types within Group C it is important to discriminate between the four main sub-groups C1 to C4.

In broad terms C1 is the most enriched sub-group with Cladophora glomerata occurring frequently which indicates nutrient enrichment, and Amblystegium fluviatile and Cinclidotus fontinaloides also occurring most frequently due to the higher base content of the rock. Reference to Fig. 5 thus shows that Group C sub-groups are prevalent where moderate to high altitude is combined with hard limestone, sandstone or Millstone Grit, as indicated by their presence in north-east Scotland, the Pennines and the North York Moors. Because the majority of Group C communities are in upland localities the rivers are typically fast flowing, dominated by bryophytes and with very few true aquatic species. Myriophyllum alterniflorum and Callitriche hamulata (Intermediate Water-starwort) are the only truly aquatic species represented in at least 20% of one or more of the three community types in Group C1.

Group C2 is a large group of oceanic river sites, usually on shales of the Ordivician and Silurian period. Although scattered throughout Britain, west Wales and south-west England are typical areas with rivers of high and moderate altitudinal sources being equally important. Although communities of Group C2 share some of the meso-eutrophic species of Group C1, they are all less important whereas more oligotrophic species are more important. Many of the rivers have densely shaded margins which favour bryophytes yet nine truly aquatic taxa occur in more than 20% of the sites of at least one of the five community types. Ranunculus penicillatus (Stream Water-crowfoot) and Oenanthe crocata (Hemlock Water-dropwort) are characteristic. Group C2 communities therefore show a reduction in both nutrient and base status, and a reduced current velocity which allows more aquatic species to occur.

Group C3 is widely distributed throughout Britain with some sub-groups being very characteristic of a particular geographical location whilst others reflect the habitat. In general all community types reflect stability, either in terms of substrate or in flow regime. For instance, some communities reflect the presence of substantial upland bogs, lakes or reservoirs, all of which stabilize flow, whereas others indicate stable earth banks or clay in the substrate. Distinct communities are found in the New Forest of Hampshire. Although bryophytes are still important, higher plants become of greater significance with 16 truly aquatic species represented in more than 20% of at least one site. Many of these species are common and includes five species not similarly represented in other sub-groups of Group C.

Group C4 are typical of oligo-mesotrophic rivers in Scotland which rise at high altitudes. Occasionally, however, rivers in the uplands of Wales or England and the less alpine rivers in northern Scotland may also be represented by these communities. Most have in common a wide margin of shingle which if stabilised will be species rich. Nine truly aquatic plants are represented with an equally rich emergent and bank flora. Bryophytes are also common but the shade loving species are less important and the species of unstable river beds and exposed shingle prevail.

GROUP D COMMUNITIES (RBSQ)

Most communities in this small group of 135 sites can be described as truly oligotrophic. However where clay is present or where upland silt accumulates in slow-flowing rivers traversing upland plains an oligo-mesotrophic flora may develop.

Geographical distribution

All Group D communities are found where solid geology and resultant soils are neutral or where Quaternary deposits are acid. Most sites are also found at high altitudes. Since there is a good correlation between an increase in altitude and a decrease in base-richness of substrates, evaluating the primary determinand of the community group is difficult. The presence of these communities in lowland peatlands of Scotland and on the Tertiary sands and heaths of the New Forest in England suggests that where acid peats and sands occur Group D communities will be present, even at low altitudes.

Almost all the streams and small rivers flowing over extensive areas of highlands and mountains in England, Wales and Scotland at altitudes above 300m (1,000 feet) will have plant communities in Group D. As a result, such communities are typical of the uplands of south-west England (Bodmin, Dartmoor and Exmoor), the highlands of Wales (Black Mountains and Cambrian mountains) the Pennines from Derbyshire to Cumbria, the North York Moors, the mountains of the Lake District and almost all the sources of rivers in Scotland except those which rise in the lowland, rich geological formations along the east coast from Berwickshire to Buchan. There are very few exceptions; these are usually due to the presence of a rich drift deposit such as clay, or a nutrient or base rich solid geological formation such as Carboniferous Limestone or sandstone which procludes the development of peat.

National Variation

Reference to Table 9 shows the range of Group D community types within the classification. These communities are exclusively found at the sources of rivers unless the river remains oligotrophic in its lower reaches. Although only six variations are recognised, Group D communities occur in more than 60 rivers in the sample. In all but three rivers, Group D communities either persist throughout the river from source to mouth (eg R. Carron, R. Oykel and R. Inver in Scotland) or gradually change to the oligo-mesotrophic communities of Group C.

The exceptions (R. Dove, R. Elwy and R. Bervie) all pass directly to the much more meso-eutrophic communities of Group B because they flow on limestone or sandstone. All fall within the same group in the classification with sources between 200-500m, flowing on limestone or sandstone and having mesotrophic chemistries.

Almost half the rivers with their uppermost sites in Group D have only this single upland site in this category. The more oligotrophic the system remains downstream, irrespective of size, the greater the extent of Group D communities. Thus the many large rivers in the sparsely cultivated areas of Scotland will remain in Group D into at least their mid-reaches.

Vegetation characteristics of Group D communities

One hundred and one taxa are represented in Table 7. This is the smallest number for the four major groups and it is also the only group in which bryophyte taxa equal the numbers of dicotyledons or monocotyledons. In addition, many bryophytes which are not easily identified have been omitted from this data set, the inclusion of which would have further illustrated their importance. There are very few purely aquatic (submerged or floating) higher plant species, Equisetum fluviatile (Water Horsetail), Callitriche hamulata (Intermediate Water-starwort), C. stagnalis (Common Water-starwort), Littorella uniflora (Shoreweed), Myriophyllum alterniflorum (Alternate-flowered Water-milfoil), Nuphar lutea (Yellow Waterlily), Juncus bulbosus (Bulbous Rush), Potamogeton polygonifolius (Bog Pondweed), Potamogeton natans (Broad-leaved Pondweed), Sparganium emersum (Unbranches Bur-reed) and Sparganium augustifolium (Floating Bur-reed) being the only eleven species which occur in at least 20% of the sites in at least one sub-group. This compares with 43 in Group A, 24 in Group B and 23 in Group C.

By reference to the Keys and Fig. 7 it is easy to see which plants are the indicator species of Group D and its six sub-groups. Reference to Table 3 shows which plants are confined to being important in Group D and Table 7 show which plants are important components in each of the six sub-groups.

The gradual decrease of trophic status from Group A to Group D is shown in Table 3. The truly oligotrophic status of Group D is shown by the absence of all those species which were common in Groups A and B and rare in Group C. Typical examples include the algae Vaucheria sessilis and Cladophora glomerata and the flowering plants Rorippa nasturtium-aquaticum (Water-cress) and Solanum dulcamara (Bitter-sweet). On the other hand, Marsupella emarginata, Blindia acuta, Schistidium agassizii, Viola palustris (Marsh Violet) and Juncus bulbosus are five examples of 22 taxa indicative of oligotrophic conditions which are restricted to being important in Group D alone.

The relative similarity of the six sub-group communities in Group D is illustrated in Table 7 which shows that approximately 40% of the taxa occur in at least 20% of the sites in all sub-groups. Both liverworts and mosses have more species common to all groups than species which show preference to particular sub-groups. Although 40% of the taxa occur in at least 20% of the sites in all the sub-groups, many of the species are indicative of particular sub-groups where they are particularly prevalent.

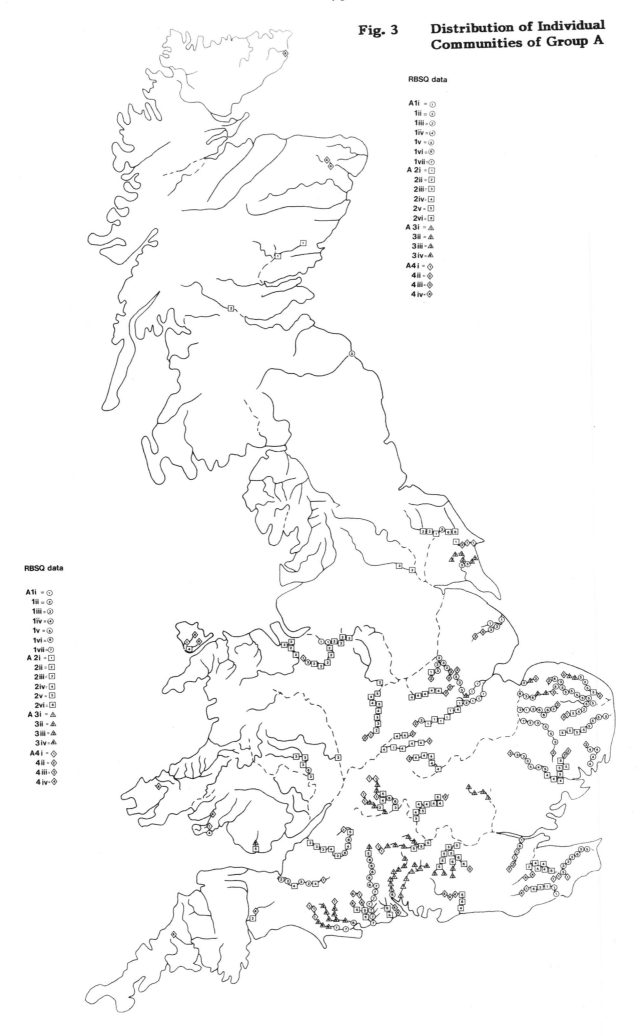

Fig. 3   Distribution of Individual Communities of Group A

RBSQ data

A1i = ①
1ii = ②
1iii = ③
1iv = ④
1v = ⑤
1vi = ⑥
1vii = ⑦
A 2i = 1
2ii = 2
2iii = 3
2iv = 4
2v = 5
2vi = 6
A 3i = △
3ii = △
3iii = △
3iv = △
A4 i = ◇
4ii = ◇
4iii = ◇
4 iv = ◇

RBSQ data

A1i = ①
1ii = ②
1iii = ③
1iv = ④
1v = ⑤
1vi = ⑥
1vii = ⑦
A 2i = 1
2ii = 2
2iii = 3
2iv = 4
2v = 5
2vi = 6
A 3i = △
3ii = △
3iii = △
3iv = △
A4 i = ◇
4ii = ◇
4iii = ◇
4 iv = ◇

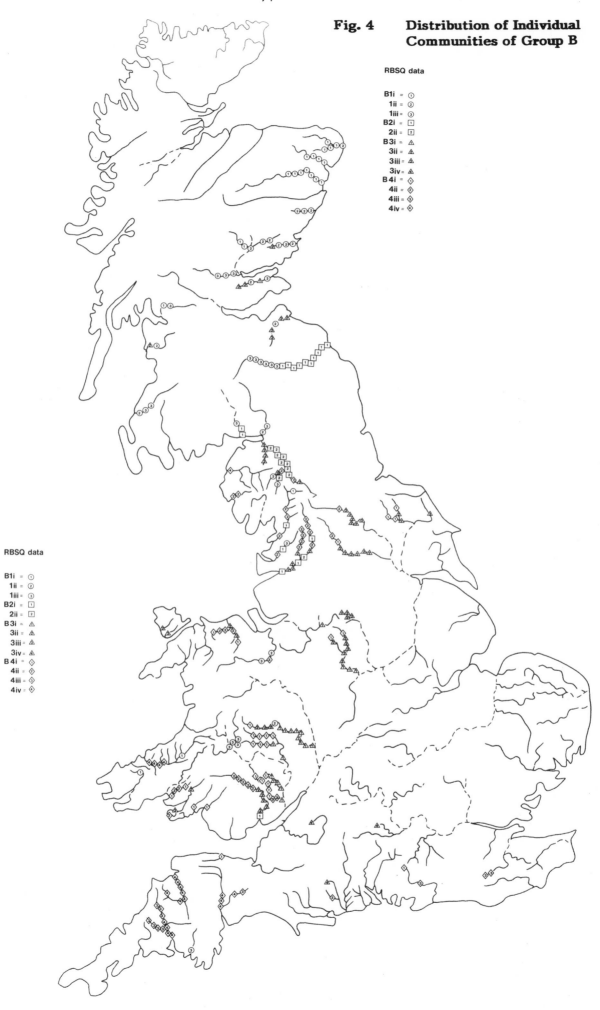

Fig. 4 **Distribution of Individual Communities of Group B**

RBSQ data

B1i = ⊙
1ii = ②
1iii = ③
B2i = ①
2ii = ②
B3i = △
3ii = △
3iii = △
3iv = △
B4i = ◇
4ii = ◇
4iii = ◇
4iv = ◇

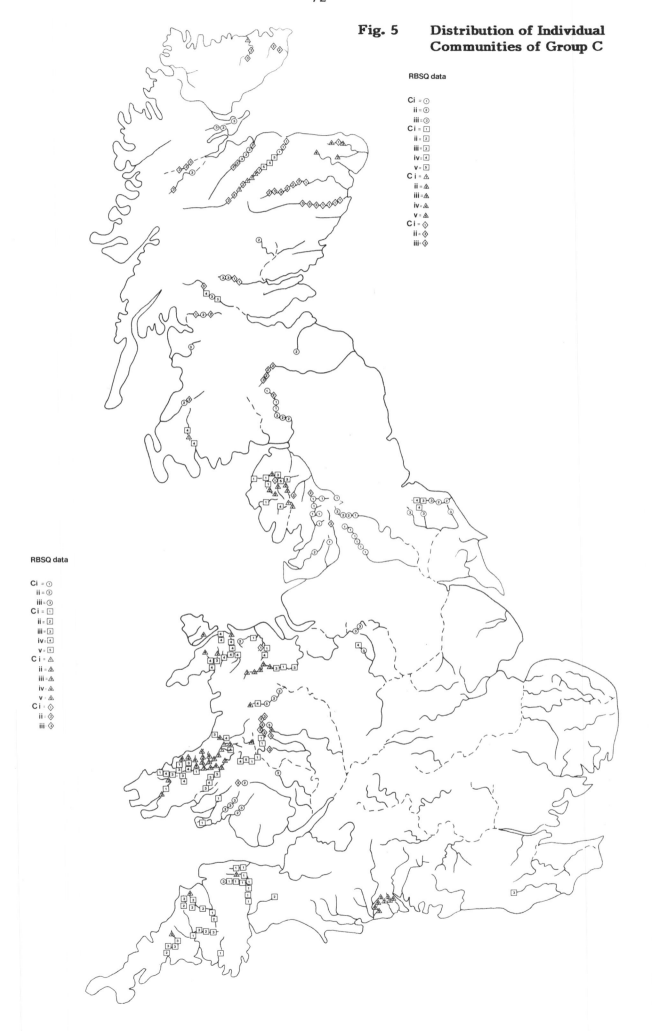

Fig. 5 **Distribution of Individual Communities of Group C**

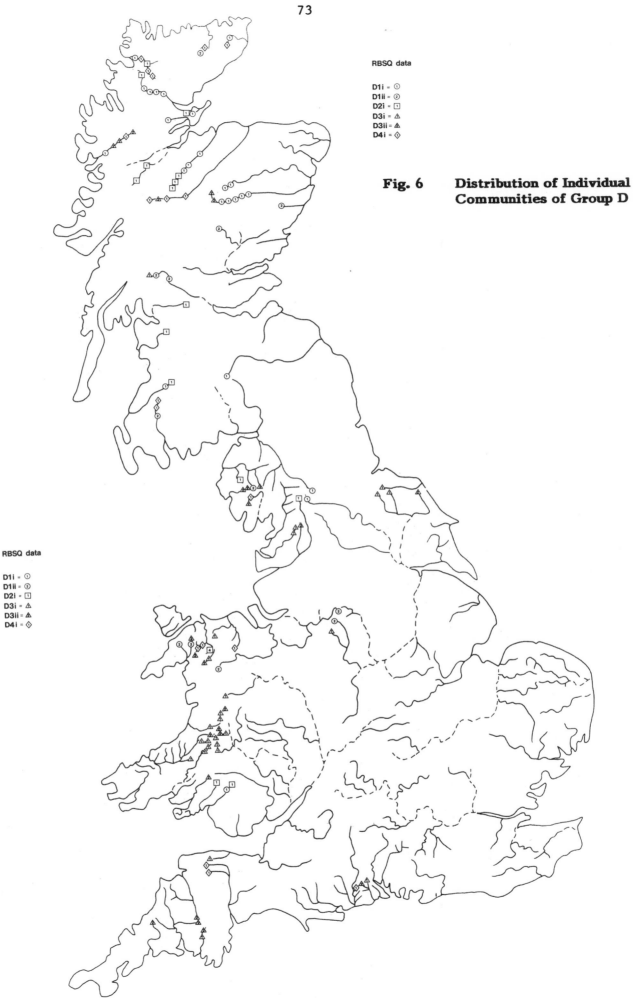

RBSQ data

D1i = ⊙
D1ii = ②
D2i = ☐
D3i = △
D3ii = ▲
D4i = ◇

Fig. 6   Distribution of Individual Communities of Group D

RBSQ data

D1i = ⊙
D1ii = ②
D2i = ☐
D3i = △
D3ii = ▲
D4i = ◇